CONCRETE
WORK
SIMPLIFIED

DONALD R. BRANN

FOURTEENTH PRINTING — 1980

REVISED EDITION

Published by

EASI-BILD DIRECTIONS SIMPLIFIED, INC.
Briarcliff Manor, NY 10510

Library of Congress Card No. 66-24876

FIRST PRINTING
© 1960

REVISED EDITIONS
1966,1969,1971,1973,
1974,1976,1979,1980

NOTE:
All metric dimensions are shown within 5/100 of a centimeter.

PUT WORRY TO WORK

If we believe God's greatest gift is time and energy, and this inheritance is ours to use as we choose, we realize why some people are luckier than others, why some win fame and fortune, and others never leave first base.

Time and energy is the world's strongest currency. It's both inflationproof and recessionproof. It is also the easiest to waste. Think of this the next time you switch on TV and spend countless hours dialing around a wasteland of nonsense, or spend equal time worrying about a problem only time can resolve.

Worrying, like spinning your wheels in mud or snow, is a habit we cultivate early in life. It wastes more of our inheritance than many realize. We don't suggest breaking this habit, we suggest harnessing it.

Remember — every thought you conceive, every move you make, is fueled by particles of time and energy in the same way gasoline powers an engine. Invest spare time making repairs or improvements, and you'll discover how to double the purchasing power of a tax shrunken buck.

This book tells how to work with concrete, how to invest time improving your home, health and mind. Just as every house requires continual care, so your mind requires continual release from tension. Working with concrete provides an economical solution to costly problems while it provides vitally needed physical exercise and mental escape.

Make this test. The next time a problem starts your worry machine, reach, read and start working on a home improvement job. Note how quickly you find relief when you refocus your Mentalens.

Don R. Brann

TABLE OF CONTENTS

It's easy when you know

Concrete work isn't difficult nor does it take a great deal of skill. It does require knowing how, plus a willingness to do what needs to be done. This book simplifies doing the various kinds of work most homeowners find necessary. Each is described and illustrated. Since each requires different steps, read the book through so you can refer to procedures pertinent to work needed to be done.

Mixing concrete requires drinking-quality water, clean sand, gravel or crushed stone. Use sand and gravel free of silt, clay and loam.

For small jobs, use the premixes. These are exactly what the name implies, an exact mixture. Add water as specified and they are ready to use. A gravel mix contains cement, sand and gravel. The gravel mix is used for concrete 2" or more thick. Ideal for setting posts, fixing large holes. A mortar mix contains cement, lime and find sand. A sand mix, cement and sand, is used for patching cracks, plastering, parging or stuccoing. 80 lbs. of premix will cover about 16 sq. ft. ¼" thick when used for plastering. The mortar mix is perfect for laying brick or blocks. Also used to repair mortar joints in chimneys, etc. Premixed concrete only requires adding water. Mix well, then use. Premixes are not recommended for large jobs.

Illus. 1 indicates mixtures recommended for use specified. For large jobs buy ready-mix. For medium size jobs, or where you can't get a ready-mix truck close enough to the work area, mix your own. Rent a mixing machine. These are great labor savors and well worth their cost.

CONCRETE MIXES

Where Used	Cubic Ft. of Sand	Cubic Ft. Gravel	Bag of Cement	Aprox. Gals. of Water
Floors, steps, walks over 2" thick	2¼	3	1	5
Footings, foundation walls, retaining walls	2¾	4	1	5½
Two course floors, pavements, flower boxes, benches, and where concrete is 2" thick.	1¾	2¼	1	4

Small amounts of concrete can be mixed in a steel wheelbarrow. Use a straight sided can or pail as a measure. One part cement, 2¼ parts of sand, 3 parts of gravel provide what is known as a 1-2-3 mix. This is an ideal mix for most improvement work.

To estimate amount of concrete needed for various size areas, multiply the width by length to obtain square footage, then note chart, Illus. 2.

CUBIC YARDS OF CONCRETE IN SLABS					
Area in square feet (length x width)	Thickness in inches				
	4	5	6	8	12
50	0.62	0.77	0.93	1.2	1.9
100	1.2	1.5	1.9	2.5	3.7
200	2.5	3.1	3.7	4.9	7.4
300	3.7	4.7	5.6	7.4	11.1
400	4.9	6.2	7.4	9.8	14.8
500	6.2	7.2	9.3	12.4	18.6

Illus. 2, indicates the number of cubic yards of concrete in slabs of different thicknesses.

Multiply length of slab by width to obtain square footage. Then read quantity of concrete according to thickness desired.

EXAMPLE: Slab is 20 x 30' by 4" thick.

Area = 20 x 30 = 600 sq. ft.

Quantity for 300 sq. ft. = 3.7 cu. yd.
2 x 3.7 = 7.4 cu. yd.

Since the table does not go as high as 600 sq. ft., use the concrete quantity for 300 sq. ft. and multiply by 2.

Use as little water as possible when mixing concrete. When mixing mortar, use water as needed to make it pliable.

Mortar is a mixture of cement and sand. Or cement, hydrated lime and sand. Mortar is used when laying brick, block or stone.

Initially, practice laying block or brick with prepared mortar mixes. These only require adding water in exact proportion directions on bag recommend, Dump the contents in a wheelbarrow, spread it out, make a hole in the middle and add as much water as directions specify. Use a hoe to pull the dry mix into the water. Or use masonry cement. One part masonry cement to two to three parts mortar sand is an acceptable mix.

Building codes frequently specify using a Type M or N mortar mix. This is what each contains.

Type M — 1 part Portland cement, ¼ part hydrated lime and not less than 2¼ or more than 3 parts sand by volume. This is a high strength mortar and is suitable for reinforced brick or block, or other masonry below grade that is in contact with the earth, i.e., foundations, retaining walls, walks, sewers, manholes, catch basins.

9

Type N — 1 part Portland cement, 1 part hydrated lime and not less than 4½ or more than 6 parts sand by volume. This mortar is considered a medium strength mortar and is recommended for exposed masonry above grade, walls, chimneys and exterior brick and block work subject to severe exposure.

Always use a batch of mortar within 2½ hours after it has been mixed. Always add water when needed. Always keep it alive by turning it over with a trowel.

MEASURING BOX

To accurately measure ingredients, build a bottomless box, Illus. 3. Cut two pieces of ½, ⅝ or ¾" plywood A, 13½ x 12"; two pieces B, 12 x 12". Apply waterproof glue and nail A to B with 8 penny common nails spaced three inches apart.

Cut two 1 x 2 x 24" for handles. Nail handles to box in position shown. Use a file or rasp to round edges. When filled level with top, measure holds one cubic foot.

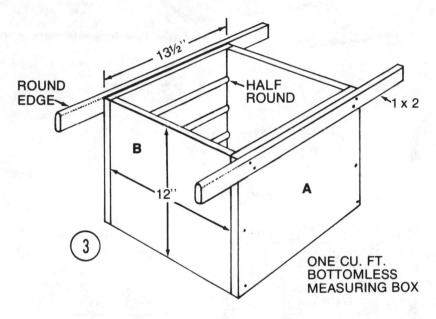

ONE CU. FT.
BOTTOMLESS
MEASURING BOX

To simplify measuring smaller quantities, nail strips of ⅜" half round to inside of box. For a quarter cubic foot, nail one strip three inches from bottom; nail another six inches from bottom for a half cubic foot; nine inches from bottom for three quarters of a cubic foot. Always place the bottomless measure in mortar tub. When you fill the amount required, remove measure.

A bag of Portland cement weighs 94 lbs.* It is equal to one cubic foot. One bag of cement, 2¼ cubic feet of sand, plus 3 cubic feet of gravel and between 4 to 5½ gallons of water makes approximately 4½ cubic feet of concrete.

*87.5 lbs. in Canada

CONCRETE MIXING TUB

You can mix concrete in an oversized wheelbarrow, or build a mixing tub, Illus. 4. Illus. 5 indicates size to cut each part.

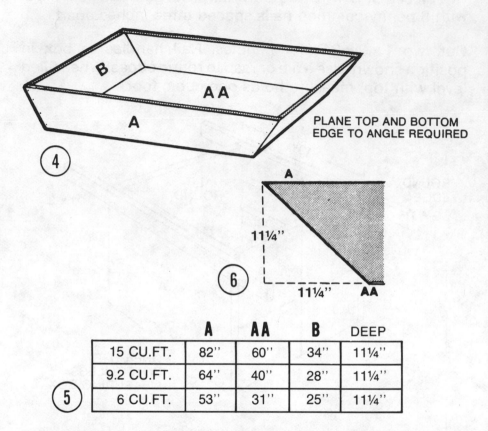

PLANE TOP AND BOTTOM
EDGE TO ANGLE REQUIRED

	A	AA	B	DEEP
15 CU.FT.	82"	60"	34"	11¼"
9.2 CU.FT.	64"	40"	28"	11¼"
6 CU.FT.	53"	31"	25"	11¼"

To build, cut two 1 x 12 by length specified for A, to angle shown, Illus. 6. Cut two ends B. Plane top and bottom edge to angle required. Apply waterproof glue and nail A to B. Apply glue and nail a 3/16" tempered hardboard panel to bottom. Always place tub on a level surface. If you use it where it needs to be supported to make level, nail an extra ⅜ or ½" plywood panel to bottom as a stiffener.

Paint tub with wood preservative. When thoroughly dry, paint inside surface with used crankcase oil. After using, always scrape out concrete. Hose tub thoroughly. When dry, paint with old crankcase oil before reusing.

12

TOOLS REQUIRED

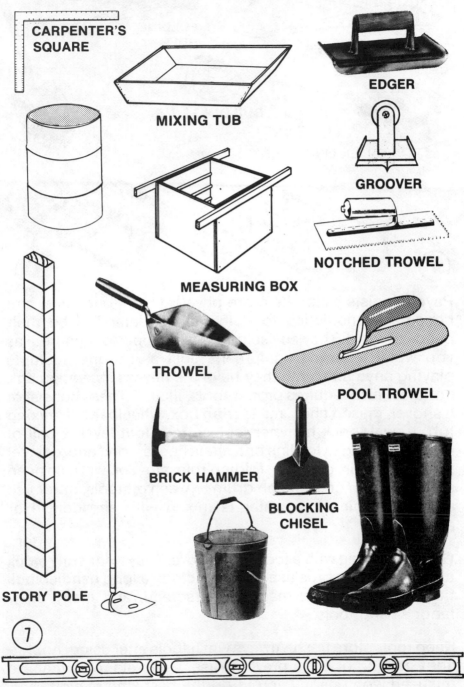

CARPENTER'S SQUARE

MIXING TUB

EDGER

GROOVER

NOTCHED TROWEL

MEASURING BOX

TROWEL

POOL TROWEL

BRICK HAMMER

BLOCKING CHISEL

STORY POLE

LEVEL

13

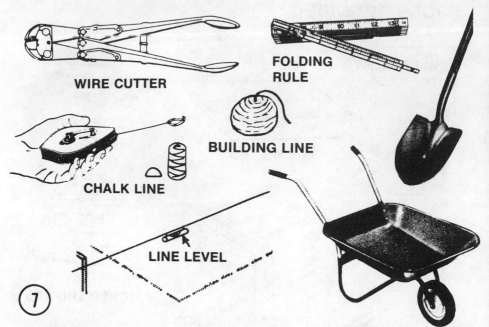

WIRE CUTTER

FOLDING RULE

BUILDING LINE

CHALK LINE

LINE LEVEL

(7)

Psychologists claim the more physical work one does, and becomes conditioned to doing, the greater will be their peace of mind. They advise purchasing tools for concrete as you would sporting equipment. Just as no one attempts playing any game until they have the necessary equipment, concrete also requires proper tools, Illus. 7. These consist of a shovel, mason't hoe, measuring box, wheelbarrow, mixing tub, trowel, brick hammer, chisel, four foot level, a ball of non-stretching nylon line or a chalk line, a wood and/or steel float, edger, groover, 6 ft. folding rule, etc. You will also need a 5 gallon can or 50 gallon drum to wash off tools, or for use as a reservoir when water is mixed with an additive or anti-freeze.

Get acquainted with a tool rental store. They frequently stock all the tools the pros use. These include a long handled bull float, roller tamper, magnesium screed, and many other labor saving tools.

Keep tools store fresh. Always wash tools after using. Apply a light coating of oil to prevent ruse. Concrete tools that are misused won't permit you to do the best kind of work.

BASIC FACTS

Always store Portland cement in a dry place. Only buy as many bags as you can use during the period you are working. Never lay bags on the ground or on a concrete floor, always on boards placed across blocks. Always cover with polyethylene when not being used. Dampness, morning dew, even humidity, can harden cement.

A mixing tub, Illus. 4, provides the best way to mix a full bag of cement. A steel wheelbarrow can be used for smaller batches. Always use up a batch of concrete as quickly as possible, preferably within 30 to 40 minutes. During hot weather, in less time.

The secret to good concrete lies in accurately measuring all material, mixing the sand and cement thoroughly to one consistent color before adding gravel. Mixing gravel, sand and cement thoroughly before adding water. Use only as much water as is needed to make a consistency that holds its shape when a handful is compressed. The exact amount of water is difficult to specify since the moisture content of sand varies.

When building a porch, patio, addition or garage adjacent to house, grade the site so water drains away from the house. If this presents a problem, buy sufficient fill to raise site. Be sure to compact dirt fill. Cover and compact at least 4'' of gravel. This must be well compacted before setting up forms for footings and foundations.

NOTE: Don't attempt a sizeable concrete job early on a hot day. Concrete sets up fast in direct sunshine. Better wait until mid-afternoon, even if it means working late in the cool of evening.

The site selected for any concrete work must be free of all foreign matter. Sod, shrubbery, stumps, etc., must be removed. Large boulders should be removed. Frost can get under a boulder and crack a footing or foundation wall. If site

15

selected has any soft spots, mud, humus, etc., remove and fill holes with gravel. Always tamp gravel to make certain it's compacted.

Always excavate area for a footing to a depth below frost level. In frost free areas, a form can be placed on any dry, compacted area that's scraped clean of greenery, stumps or growth. Never build a form or lay concrete over a recently filled area. Never throw dirt back into an excavated area. If you find it necessary to fill in, use gravel. Always tamp gravel. If site is compacted but wet, remove soft spots, spread and tamp gravel. Never lay concrete in mud. To eliminate settling, compact gravel over entire length of footing. Embed ½" reinforcing rods in position shown, Illus. 8. Overlap ends of rods at least 4". Use 2 x 6 or 2 x 8 rather than 2 x 4 for footing forms.

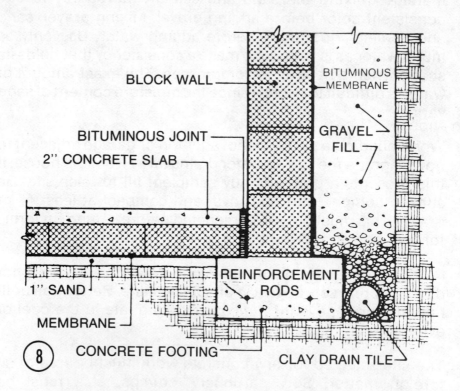

BLOCK WALL

BITUMINOUS MEMBRANE

BITUMINOUS JOINT

2" CONCRETE SLAB

GRAVEL FILL

1" SAND

REINFORCEMENT RODS

MEMBRANE

8

CONCRETE FOOTING

CLAY DRAIN TILE

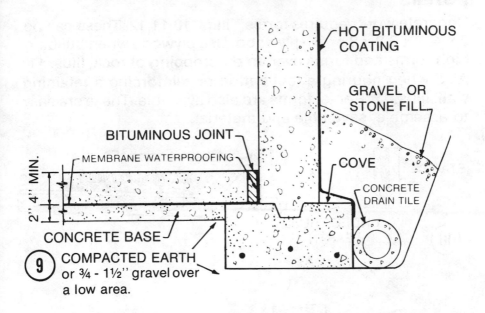

HOT BITUMINOUS COATING

GRAVEL OR STONE FILL

BITUMINOUS JOINT

MEMBRANE WATERPROOFING

COVE

2" 4" MIN.

CONCRETE DRAIN TILE

CONCRETE BASE

9 COMPACTED EARTH or ¾ - 1½'' gravel over a low area.

Never lay footings, or block, in freezing weather unless anti-freeze is mixed with the water, and the work is covered at night to protect against freezing.

Those wishing to lay a wood floor and/or regular carpeting in a basement should embed 2 x 3 or 2 x 4 sleepers, 16'' on centers, Illus. 43, when pouring the top slab. These permit nailing wood flooring or exterior grade plywood. Use pressure treated lumber, or apply a wood preservative before placing in position. Drive 8 penny common nails part way in side of sleepers. This locks sleeper to concrete. Check sleepers with a straight edge and level in two directions. Pour concrete level with sleeper. Allow concrete to cure thoroughly, then mop hot tar or asphalt paint over entire area. Allow to dry thoroughly before nailing flooring or plywood. If you plan on laying carpeting over an existing concrete floor, cement underlayment recommended by carpet retailer to floor, then lay indoor/outdoor carpeting.

17

FORMS

Concrete work requires forms,* Illus. 10,11,12. These can be 2 x 4, 2 x 6, 2 x 8 or ⅝" plywood. Use plywood when building high forms and forms over an outcropping of rock, Illus. 11. Also when pouring a foundation or reinforcing a retaining wall, Illus. 12. Rental forms are also available. These are easy to assemble, save time and material.

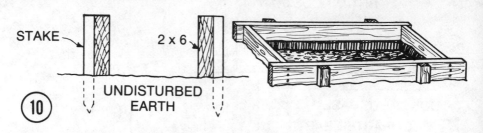

STAKE   2 x 6

UNDISTURBED EARTH

(10)

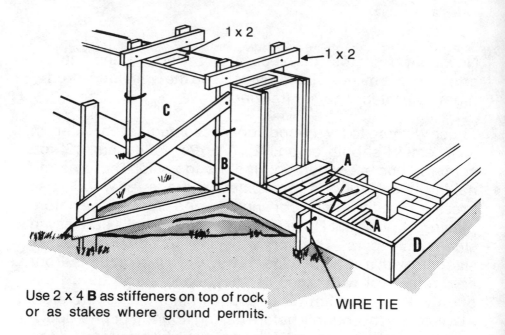

1 x 2

1 x 2

C

B

A

A

D

Use 2 x 4 **B** as stiffeners on top of rock, or as stakes where ground permits.

WIRE TIE

(11)

A — 1 x 2
B — 2 x 4
C — PLYWOOD
D — 2 x 4, 2 x 6, 2 x 8

*Book #697 Forms, Footings, Foundations, Framing, Stair Building describes commercial type forms that can be rented.

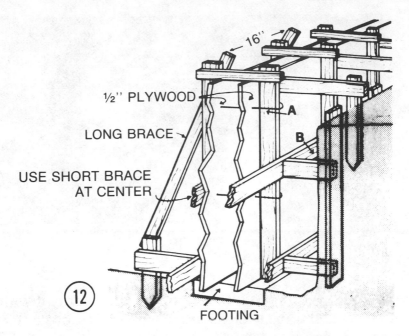

16"

½" PLYWOOD

A

LONG BRACE

B

USE SHORT BRACE
AT CENTER

⑫

FOOTING

Prior to pouring a basement floor, garage or any slab subject to dampness, raise area with 1½ and 3/4" gravel to a height at least equal to drain tile around perimeter, Illus. 9.

After compacting gravel, spread a polyethylene waterproof membrane over entire area. Allow membrane to cover side of footings, Illus. 8, 13, before placing expansion joint in place. Use care not to puncture polyethylene. Buy width and length required to lay membrane in one piece.

⑬ GRAVEL WATERPROOF MEMBRANE 6 x 6" WIRE

(13) CONCRETE

Concrete requires time to cure. Indoors spray it with a fine mist at least once every 24 hours. Outdoors, protect from the heat of the sun. Cover with roofing felt, building paper, burlap, etc. Remove same before spraying.

All slabs of concrete should be reinforced with 6 x 6" reinforcing wire. This is spread over polyethylene and raised (use globs of concrete) to center of slab, Illus. 13, 16.

ELECTRICALLY WELDED WIRE FABRIC REINFORCING

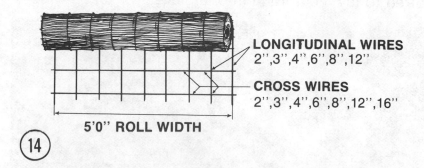

LONGITUDINAL WIRES
2",3",4",6",8",12"

CROSS WIRES
2",3",4",6",8",12",16"

5'0" ROLL WIDTH

(14)

Welded wire reinforcing is available in five foot width. Reinforcing rods come in No. 2, 3 and 4 sizes, Illus. 15.

20

REINFORCING RODS

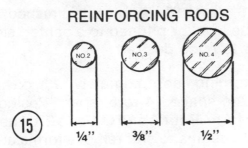

Use 2 x 4's sharpened at end for form stakes. If you build a large form, rent iron stakes. Only toenail form to wood stakes. Use wire to hold form with iron stakes. This permits removing form without disturbing concrete.

When laying a floor where you can't finish the entire job in one pouring, divide the area with forms, Illus. 16.

Build sections to size you can handle. A 4 to 6' wide form is an easy size for two men to screed. First pour A-C. Allow to set. Remove a, fill with concrete. Remove b,c,d and fill form B-D.

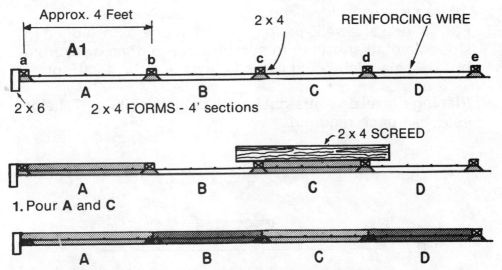

1. Pour **A** and **C**

2. Remove forms and pour sections **B** and **D**. Fill in area between **A-1** and form. Second pouring is indicated by darker shading.

Top edge of 2 x 6, Illus. 16, represents finished height of floor. These can be level or pitched to a center, side or end drain (⅛ to 1") or to pitch desired.

Raise wire reinforcing approximately 2" on globs of concrete. 2 x 4's are spaced 4 to 6' apart. Position a 2 x 4 alongside outside form. Pour A and C. Use a 2 x 4 as a screed. When the concrete begins to set, remove forms and pour B and D. Fill in area between A1 and form. The second pouring is indicated by darker shading.

Straight lengths of 1 x 6, 2 x 4, 2 x 6, other dimension lumber or plywood may be used for forms. Always sight down the edge of a board. Note whether the edge is straight, raised, or contains a low spot. Use only straight edged lumber as the top edge dictates shape of finished floor or footings.

Always check forms with a level. While you must build a rigid form, never drive nails all the way. Allow sufficient projection so nails can be pulled without disturbing concrete.

All forms must be level and plumb, or slope to pitch desired. Forms for a sidewalk, patio or porch floor are positioned to slope amount specified to permit water to drain away from house. This pitch could be as little as ⅛ to ¼" to a foot.

Placing a level on a straight length of lumber, Illus. 17, helps establish pitch required.

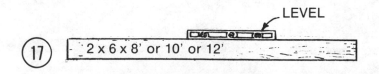

LEVEL

(17) 2 x 6 x 8' or 10' or 12'

When digging a trench for footings, always dig to a depth below frost level. Lay footings to height that provides space for number of block courses required.

Forms for a garage floor should slope toward a center, side or end drain. The pitch can be ⅛'' to a foot. The drain should be connected to a dry well, Illus. 18. Locate this at a sufficient distance, depth and size so water will not back up.

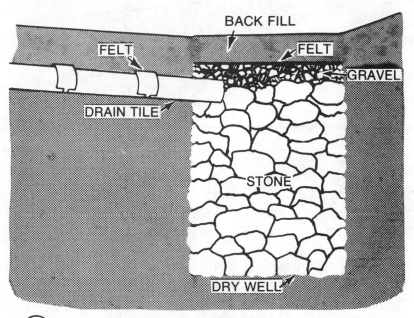

BACK FILL

FELT

FELT

GRAVEL

DRAIN TILE

STONE

DRY WELL

(18)   Concrete blocks laid up dry, no mortar, can also be used for a dry well.

Depending on weather, concrete begins to set within a couple of hours, but takes days to cure. When pouring a section where you want to remove a form as quickly as concrete begins to set, predrill one side and drive nails into adjoining part. Never drive nails all the way. This simplifies removal of form without disturbing concrete.

When pouring a large area in sections, always wet area of existing concrete before pouring adjacent batch. If one section has set, you can make a better bond by painting edge with a wet mix consisting of I part cement to 2 parts sand.

When building a form where it isn't possible to drive stakes, use wire spreaders, Illus. 11,12,19, or 1 x 2's to both spread and hold form together.

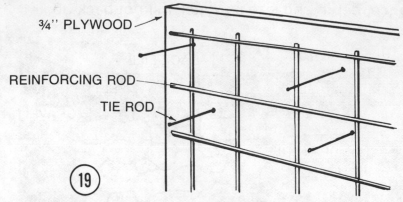

¾" PLYWOOD

REINFORCING ROD

TIE ROD

19

Holes for wire spreaders are usually drilled two feet on centers. Spreaders are placed where needed to allow form to contain concrete without bulging. Use 2 x 4, 2 x 6, 2 x 8 for forms. Position 1 x 2 or 2 x 4 stakes every 6'.

Always tamp concrete in a form. Many masons wear 16" high rubber boots and tamp a slab by walking. If you plan a career doing masonry work, buy or rent a tamper, Illus. 20. These are available 36 and 48" in width. It brings fine material to the surface while it compacts the larger aggregates. Tamping can also be done by shoving a 1 x 4 or 2 x 4 into newly poured concrete to eliminate air pockets adjacent to a form or corner.

20

Magnesium concrete rakes, Illus. 21, are great work savers. These are available with extra long handles. They help amateurs work like pros when laying a large area. Use the teeth for spreading, the smooth edge for screeding and floating. These are available at rental stores.

Always fill a form to top edge, then screed concrete level, Illus. 16. Use a 2 x 4 or other straight edge. Screeding any area larger than a footing form requires one man at each end of a screed. Work it back and forth. Always fill low spots with concrete.

Illus. 22 shows ½" steel reinforcing rods centered in form. These are wired together 1'0" verticaly and horizontally.

Use ⅝ or ¾" plywood for forms. Stiffen with 2 x 4 A, 2'0" on centers, Illus. 12.

2 x 4's B, spaced 2'0" on centers horizontaly, hold forms together. Steel ties C, available from your masonry supply dealer, are positioned 2'0" on centers. These hold forms securely in place. When you strip forms, cut ties flush with concrete. Use wire cutters.

When building a foundation containing a window, door or other opening, use ties at corners, also every two feet.

When laying a slab in a basement, garage, porch or patio adjacent to a house foundation, allow for an expansion joint, Illus. 23, between slab and foundation. Use ½ or ¾" asphalt impregnated insulation board cut to thickness of slab. Place in position shown around perimeter.

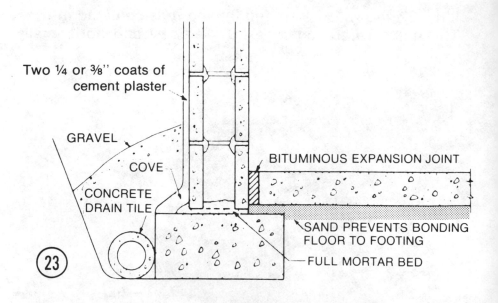

Two ¼ or ⅜" coats of cement plaster

GRAVEL

COVE

CONCRETE DRAIN TILE

23

BITUMINOUS EXPANSION JOINT

SAND PREVENTS BONDING FLOOR TO FOOTING

FULL MORTAR BED

Place an expansion joint between a poured sidewalk and house foundation, between a driveway and garage foundation, etc.

(24)

Contraction joints, Illus. 24, are formed by cutting a groove 1'' deep across a slab. Allow concrete to set up sufficiently to support a 2 x 8 plank. Use this as a straight edge to guide a groover, Illus. 25. This permits concrete to shrink in cold weather without cracking.

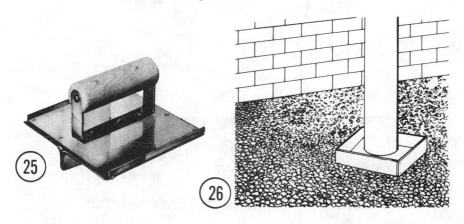

(25) (26)

When laying a walk or driveway, contraction joints are usually spaced every four to six feet.

Always isolate footings for a steel column with an expansion joint around four sides, Illus. 26.

To keep out cold, many professionals cover foundation with asphalt impregnated board. This is placed in position, Illus. 27. The soil and gravel are compacted and the slab poured over polyethylene.

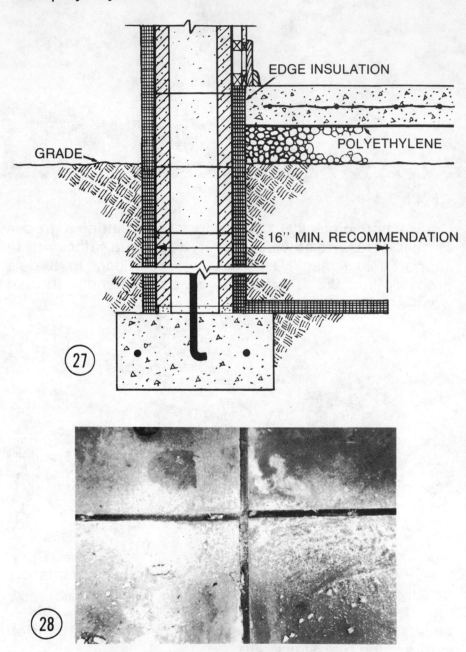

EDGE INSULATION

POLYETHYLENE

GRADE

16" MIN. RECOMMENDATION

27

28

When laying large areas, divide it, Illus. 16,28, into size sections you can easily pour and screed. Use a line and line level to make certain forms are level or at pitch desired. In this application, the asphalt impregnated strips, embedded between sections, are called control joints. These remain permanently embedded.

Use ¾, 1" or thicker rigid asphalt impregnated insulation, or fiber glass board. Cut to width equal to thickness of slab edgewise, Illus. 29. Also cut pieces 16" by length required. Lay in position shown, end to end, completely around perimeter.

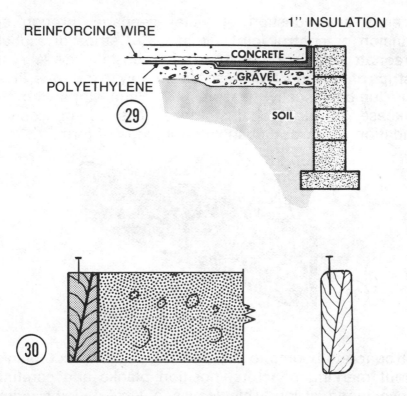

REINFORCING WIRE   1" INSULATION

CONCRETE

POLYETHYLENE   GRAVEL

29   SOIL

30

Two lengths of beveled clapboard, Illus. 30, placed in position shown, can also be used to form an expansion joint. Paint with motor oil. Drive 8 penny nails in one thick butt edge, every 4'. This permits removal as soon as concrete begins to set. When concrete has cured, fill slot with hot tar or other bituminous joint filler, Illus. 31.

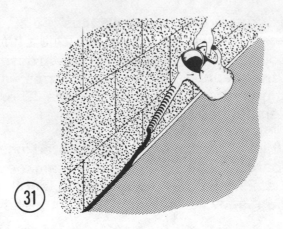

If there's any question of water seepage through an expansion or control joint, do this. Cut strips of asphalt impregnated insulation board to width of slab, less ¾". Cut ½" strips of 1" wood. Nail these temporarily to top edge, Illus. 32. 1" lumber usually measures ¾". Paint strips with old crankcase oil. Place against forms, Illus. 23, or existing foundation with wood flush with top edge of form.

WOOD STRIP

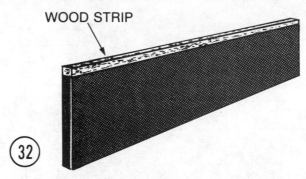

After concrete begins to set, and will support 2 x 8 planks without marking concrete, position planks and carefully remove wood strips. This leaves a ½ x ¾" joint. Allow concrete to cure for at least a week, then fill joint with bituminous sealant sold by your building material dealer. Hot tar can also be poured into crack, Illus. 31. When dry, sprinkle dry cement over joint.

ADDITIVES, WATERPROOFING, HARDENERS

A concrete slab can be hardened, made comparatively non-dusting, and waterproofed with the addition of Anti Hydro Set or equal additive.

This is a good investment when pouring a basement or floor area where there's any question of dampness. It's also recommended in garages and commercial work where a thoroughly hardened and non-dusting floor is desirable.

Follow manufacturer's directions and add the exact amount of additive they specify to the water when mixing concrete. In the case of ready mix, always pour in the exact gallons of additive required according to the size of the load. Besides waterproofing, these additives act as hardeners and dust inhibitors.

Measure and mix additive in exact amount of water manufacturer specifies. Then use only as much of this water to a bag of cement as specified. Saw the top off a 50 gallon drum and use as a reservoir for premixed water. If you buy ready mix, add additive to tank and make certain it's mixed thoroughly before driver starts to pour.

GENERAL PROCEDURE

Pouring concrete follows this procedure. After excavating and removing all foreign matter, spread and compact gravel. Set up forms and guide lines. Check lines with a line level, Illus. 33. When pouring concrete against existing concrete or stone, paint concrete with a wet mixture of one part cement to two parts sand.

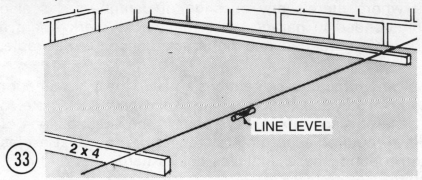

After filling a form, tamp to compact as previously described. The more you compact concrete, the harder it will be. Concrete in small forms can be compacted with a 2 x 4.

Tool rental stores stock machine driven tampers. These are especially handy when compacting a large area, subject to heavy loads or traffic.

When you have filled and compacted a form, use a straight edged 2 x 4 as a screed, Illus. 34. Work it back and forth, saw fashion, to level concrete flush with edge of form.

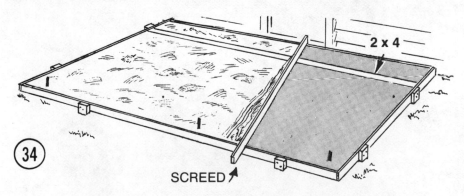

Floating, Illus. 35, can be done with a wood float for a course texture. Use a steel float for smoother surface. The wood float produces a gritty, non-slip surface while a steel float, Illus. 36, produces a mirror smooth finish.

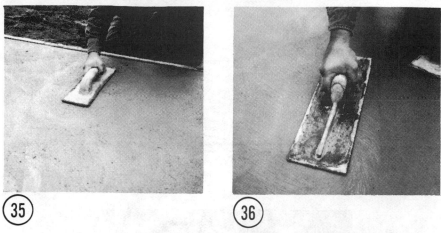

A rougher surface can be produced by using a hair broom, Illus. 37; while a course brush broom, Illus. 38, produces an even rougher surface.

When working on a large area, rent a long handled magnesium bull float, Illus. 39. You can also rent finishing brooms with extension handles.

Depending on the weather, concrete frequently begins to set within an hour. Cut outside edge free from form using a steel float or trowel, Illus. 40. Finish edge with edger, Illus. 41. This insures a smooth, compacted, rounded edge when form is removed. A long handled edger can be rented, Illus. 42.

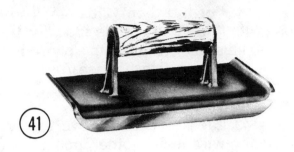

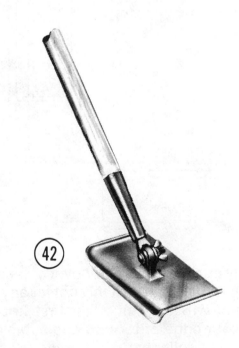

FLOORS OVER WET AREAS

If there's any question concerning underground water or surface seepage draining into site, select a new site. If this isn't possible, lay stone or sufficient fill to raise site to divert surface drainage. Compact fill thoroughly. Since water is tricky, take this precaution. Set a 12" diameter by 2' tile vertically in one corner of the room, Illus. 44. Top of tile should finish flush with floor. Use size tile specified by sump pump manufacturer, Illus. 45. Cap tile with a plywood disc. If it's ever needed, you will appreciate the ease in which a sump pump can be installed.

Lay a sub-slab, Illus. 43. Lay 1" of concrete over a gravel bed, and spread reinforcing wire. Lay another inch of concrete. Screed concrete flush with top of footing. Allow to cure thoroughly. Fill expansion joint with hot tar.

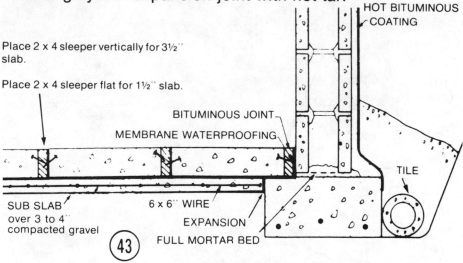

Place 2 x 4 sleeper vertically for 3½" slab.

Place 2 x 4 sleeper flat for 1½" slab.

HOT BITUMINOUS COATING

BITUMINOUS JOINT

MEMBRANE WATERPROOFING

TILE

SUB SLAB over 3 to 4" compacted gravel

6 x 6" WIRE

EXPANSION

FULL MORTAR BED

(43)

When thoroughly cured, mop hot tar over sub-slab, top edge of footing and up foundation 6". Only hot tar an area 2" wider than first course of #15 felt. Embed the first strip of felt up 6" on foundation, over edge of footing and sub-slab. Use care not to tear felt. Rent a roller to make certain felt is completely bonded. Paint 2" wide band of first strip with hot tar so you can overlap next strip 2". Bond felt to sub-slab east to west, then follow same procedure north to south. Allow to dry.

Place expansion joint in position; use beveled siding or asphalt impregnated insulation board and proceed to lay top slab as previously described. Use care not to bruise membrane.

HOW TO INSTALL A SUMP PUMP

In many basements a sump pump is as necessary as a bilge pump in a boat. If a spring thaw or unseasonally heavy downpour creates underground pressure, a sump pump can usually handle the situation.

If you need to cut a hole through an existing floor, carefully check the floor with a level and straight edge to make certain you select lowest point. Use a chisel and hammer to break a hole in floor. Renting an electric hammer is a good idea. Since these work fast, rent by the hour. Make certain no water, electric, sewer or heating lines are embedded in floor. Cut hole to size and depth sump pump manufacturer recommends. Most manufacturers recommend filling bottom of hole with 3 to 4" of gravel, then placing an 8 or 12" diameter drain tile vertically in position, Illus. 44. Back fill around tile with gravel, repair floor with concrete. Top of tile should finish flush with floor, then be covered with a plywood disc cut to size tile requires.

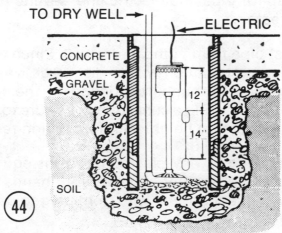

TO DRY WELL → ELECTRIC
CONCRETE
GRAVEL
12"
14"
SOIL
44

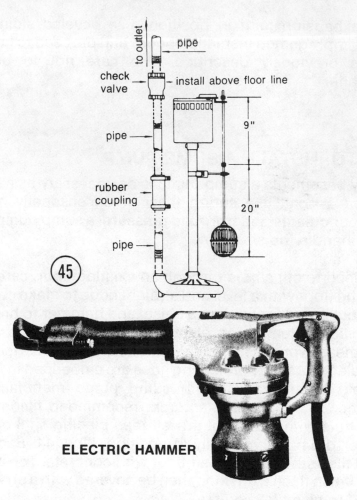

to outlet

pipe

check
valve

install above floor line

9"

pipe

rubber
coupling

20"

pipe

45

pipe

ELECTRIC HAMMER

Drill holes in cap for pipe and electric line, several more to allow well to breathe.

Connect exhaust pipe from pump to dry well. Since you will have to go through foundation wall to discharge water to a dry well, drill a hole through foundation at the highest possible point. When buying a sump pump, be sure to obtain one that will "lift" water to height your foundation requires.

CAUTION: Never plug in any electrical tool or equipment when you are working in water, or when your hands or feet are wet. Always connect ground wire from plug to cover on receptacle.

38

WATERPROOFING BASEMENTS

As with most problems, there are many solutions. To intelligently cure a wet basement, you must first determine the cause. If you purchased a house that has a sump pump, assume the former owner, even the builder, had a problem with water. If a leak has only recently developed, it could be caused by a blocked downspout from a gutter, a crack in a gutter, overflow from a septic tank, new construction or landscaping around a house on adjacent property. When adjacent land is bulldozed or excavated, it frequently alters the course of surface drainage. This can even happen when neighboring property is only slightly reshaped.

Houses built on a slab, no basement, in areas serviced by septic tanks, sometimes experience an odor no rose can cure. This can be traced to an overflow, or blockage in the field tile servicing a septic tank, yours, or a neighbors.

NOTE: Those about to buy a house should "smell" basement air. Note whether an air purifier or a fan is being used. Always look for water stains on concrete floors and walls. The best time to do this is before, and again after a heavy rainfall. If you like the house, but sense a problem of dampness, even though you can't see much evidence, to alleviate any suspicion, ask the owner to run a garden hose on one side of a roof for at least a half hour, and again on the other side. If there's no problem, the owner won't hesitate to comply.

Those considering purchase of a house built on a slab in a low lying area should look for water stains in a furnace room or any concrete floor that has a floor drain. Few potential home buyers think to inspect a house with their nose and yet the nose tells much.

While the time to waterproof a basement is when the house is under construction, leaks frequently occur in areas where only a small part of the basement is underground. When you find evidence of a leak, excavate wall to a depth below leak. Waterproof outside wall as described on page 42.

To solve the problem working from within, you have to carefully inspect all walls and floor area. Remove all loose mortar in joints. Inspect the wall for cracks. Note area around any service line entering the basement, i.e., water line, underground cable, etc.

If you don't locate a leak during a wet period, allow basement to dry. During the first dry spell, inspect the gutters and downspouts. Even if they appear in good shape, play a hose on the roof to create the effect of a heavy rain. After determining gutters and downspouts are not the cause, dig down to depth of footings, Illus. 23, to ascertain whether the builder installed 4" drain tiles. You may find one or more blocked. Flood the hole. See if water seeps into basement.

Four inch drain tiles placed in position indicated and sloped toward a dry well located away, and at a depth lower than basement floor and footings, will normally keep a floor dry. Tiles should be covered with a 4 to 6" bed of ¾ to 1½" gravel.

Masonry paint and latex sealants are now available that seal the surface of a concrete floor and block wall and prevent water from entering. Sealants containing Portland cement and synthetic rubber can be used to prevent water, even under pressure, from entering a basement. Apply these exactly as manufacturer specifies.

Be sure to check area around a chimney for cracks or from settling. Chimneys frequently settle after a severe cold snap. Seal even the smallest crack with acrylic latex sealant after removing all loose mortar. Mix mortar with waterproofing additive. Follow manufacturer's directions. Use a wood or metal float, Illus. 46. Pack mortar in joint. Use a jointer, Illus. 47, to pack and finish edge.

Many fast setting sealants can be applied over a wet wall or floor. First wire brush area. Hose away dust and loose particles.

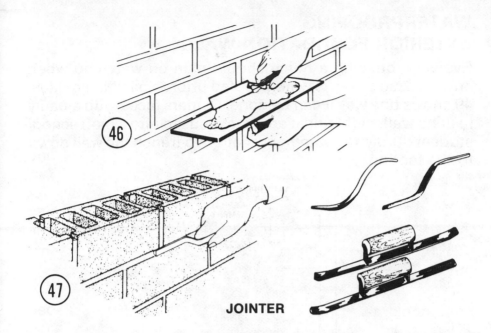

JOINTER

If you are attempting to waterproof a floor where there's water, the water should be pumped out, and kept out. Allow waterproofing compound to set for at least 24 hours.

Many surface cracks can be waterproofed with an acrylic latex concrete crack sealant, Illus. 48. Some can be applied with a calking gun. Hose out loose particles, dirt and dust. Fill crack flush with surface. Acrylic latex sealant makes a chemical bond to concrete.

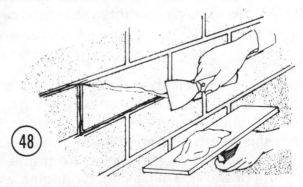

Where a crack contains water that can't be drained, use a plug sealant. Those made from Portland cement and synthetic rubber can be applied to a wet surface.

WATERPROOFING
EXTERIOR FOUNDATION WALL

Everyone building a home should plan on watching when and if a foundation is waterproofed prior to backfilling. Illus. 49 shows one way it can be done. Owners faced with a badly leaking wall might find it advantageous to hire a high school student during the summer vacation to trench the wall down to the footing.

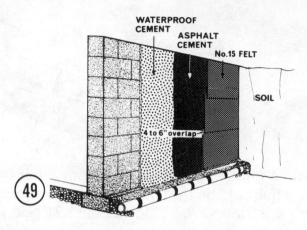

Allow all dirt on wall to dry, then wire brush. Hose the wall and allow to dry. Wire brush and hose a second time to remove all dirt from mortar joints.

Lay a bed of gravel and 4" tile end to end along footing, Illus. 43. Slope tile ⅛" per foot. Wrap joints with strips of #15 felt. Carefully cover tile with 2" of ¾" gravel. Cover gravel with #15 felt.

When wall is dry, completely free of dust and dirt, spray with water. While wet, brush on a slush coat consisting of one part Portland cement, one part Anti Hydro to three parts water, Illus. 50. Paint this over dampened surface. While still wet, apply a ⅜" thick cement mortar mixed from one part Anti Hydro to 10 parts of water. This is called gauging water. Mix one part Portland cement to two parts of clean sand. Add gauging water. Apply a ⅜" thick coating, Illus. 51, to a foot above grade line. When this coat begins to set, scratch it,

Illus. 51. Use a trowel or screwdriver. Allow it to cure for about a week. Spray it each day with a fine mist to insure proper curing. Prior to applying a finishing coat, spray wall. Apply a ⅜" finishing coat, Illus. 52. Use the same mix as scratch coat. Smooth finish this coat. When thoroughly cured and dry, apply asphalt cement, Illus. 53. Embed #15 felt horizontally in the wet asphalt. Start at bottom and overlap each course 6", Illus. 49.

Apply a finishing coat of hot tar or asphalt cement to thoroughly seal all joints. While this provides a method of waterproofing an outside wall, it does very little to insulate from the cold.

Basements where condensation creates a problem can now be solved with a number of different types of sealants. Moisture build up on a block or poured concrete foundation can frequently be remedied by placing rigid foam or fiber glass insulation against the outside wall, Illus. 54.

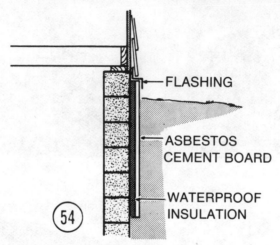

Use 1, 2" or thickness required to protect against temperature in area. This insulation should be bonded to wall with asphalt cement and should cover wall to a depth below frost level. Cover insulation with ¼" asbestos cement board. Cut a strip of aluminum or copper flashing. Insert flashing under siding, or under siding starter strip, then bend it over asbestos cement panel board. This keeps rain from penetrating insulation. Backfill by hand. Use care not to break asbestos cement board or insulation.

WATER SEEPAGE

Water entering a basement can usually be traced to either a concealed or exposed crack in mortar joints, cracked blocks, or from pressure building up alongside or under basement floor. Two of the most common causes are:

1. A poorly installed leader carrying water from gutters. If leader is clogged, a joint loose, or leader discharges too close to foundation wall, it creates problems that can easily be rectified.

2. Hard to find hairline cracks in mortar joints can frequently be located when you apply sufficient water at grade level.

Check each leader to make certain it drains away from foundation to either a run off, or to a dry well. If you build a dry well, do so far enough from foundation and at a level that can absorb it.

Seepage through cracks in mortar joints can be sealed in several different ways. If crack starts near grade level, Illus. 55, dig a trench with bottom of trench level with crack. Cover side, but not bottom of trench with polyethylene.* Soak trench with water so it filters into, and soaks crack. Next pour in Hydro Stop or equal ready to use liquid sealant. Pour sealant into trench and it will seep into and fill crack. Since there are many different types of liquid sealants available, follow manufacturer's directions.

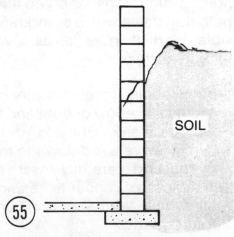

SOIL

55

*Polyethylene wrappers from your dry cleaner can be used.

Keep pouring sealant into trench until foundation refuses to absorb it. Wait awhile, then apply a fine mist of water and flush any sealant remaining in trench. Some of this will be absorbed by foundation.

Some hairline cracks frequently require a second application. Apply same 24 hours later. Again, wet trench with water to soak crack before applying second application.

If a crack starts below grade, where it's concealed on the outside by a concrete walk, but shows up inside basement, you can waterproof it in two ways. Using a carbide tipped masonry bit, Illus. 56, rout out mortar at least ½ to ¾" deep where crack appears. Remove all loose particles. If you don't have an electric drill, borrow one, or use a can opener. Make a V groove ½ to ¾" deep the full length of crack.

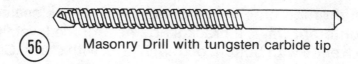

(56)   Masonry Drill with tungsten carbide tip

Apply a paste sealant, either latex or epoxy, Illus. 48. Latex base patching material comes in two parts, a liquid latex and a dry powder. Mix only as much as you can apply immediately after mixing. This paste sets fast — some within two minutes, so follow manufacturer's directions, and you'll waterproof like a "pro." Apply patching paste with a putty knife. Working as quickly as possible, work it in as far as it will go and smooth it over flush with surface.

If this doesn't solve your problem, locate position of crack on inside by measuring over to a window or door and from top of foundation down. Do same outside. Drill a ½" or larger hole through concrete, Illus. 57. Drive a rod down to a depth just above crack. Remove rod and carefully insert a piece of copper tubing. Fasten a piece of rubber hose and funnel to top end, Illus. 58. Fill funnel with water. When crack is saturated, pour in liquid sealant.

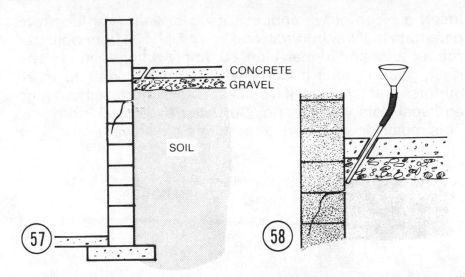

CONCRETE
GRAVEL

SOIL

(57)

(58)

If you have a long crack, or if a portion of the foundation wall is allowing water to enter at several different levels, draw a chart to accurately locate area. Drive a crow bar or iron rod to each depth and service each crack.

Cracks that take in a lot of water should be sealed inside with paste sealant, and on outside with liquid sealer.

Another way of filling a crack below grade in a poured concrete wall, one that shows up on inside of basement, Illus. 59, is by drilling a ½" or larger hole at top of crack. Drill hole at a slight downward angle to a distance halfway through wall. Use a ½" or larger masonry bit.

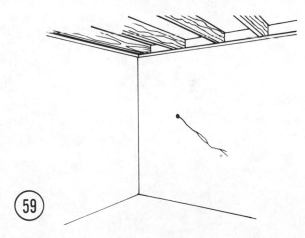

(59)

Insert a piece of ½" copper tubing of sufficient length to penetrate halfway into wall and still project 2" from wall. Use rubber tube and funnel, Illus. 60. Apply water, then sealant. Keep pouring until it won't take any more. Wait 15 to 20 minutes and try again. If it still won't take more, remove pipe and seal hole with an epoxy or latex base patching paste. This repair doesn't work in concrete block walls.

POURED CONCRETE

60

Even where there's underground water pressure, your masonry supply retailer can recommend a sealant. Some fast setting sealants, available in powder form, are mixed with water. It dries to a hard metallic finish in minutes. These plug sealants can also be used to anchor bolts, fasteners or iron railings in concrete. Only mix as much as you need. Don't mix a new batch with any part of a previous batch. Most patching plug sealants are applied to a thoroughly soaked surface. Use a short bladed putty knife. Work the sealant in fast, deep and smooth, as quickly as possible.

LAYING CONCRETE BLOCKS

Laying blocks for a wall requires:

1. Selecting a site that's within your property line, one that doesn't block a natural run off of water; or divert water toward neighboring property.

2. Clearing area, establishing a grade level, setting up batter boards and guide lines* and excavating to a depth below frost level.

3. Erecting forms and pouring footings, Illus. 61.

If your plans require installation of water, electric, gas or telephone lines through foundation, make an open end box from four pieces of 2 x 6 or 2 x 8 x 16". Water lines must be installed below frost level. A 4" diameter drain tile, Illus. 61, can also be used. Place in position indicated. Be sure to mark location and depth of opening on foundation plan. If you use lumber for a form, knock out the form after concrete has set.

Always purchase extra blocks to allow for breakage. When necessary, make heavier mortar joints between blocks to fill space available. When estimating the number of blocks required, figure three 16" blocks per course to every four feet.

4. Locate exact corners. Drop a plumb bob down from guide lines.

5. Lay out a course of block dry, no mortar, to establish exact number of blocks needed for first course, corner to corner. Use ⅜" pieces of plywood for a ⅜" thick mortar joint; ½" pieces for ½" joints. ⅜" is the preferred size. Cut a block if necessary.

Use end blocks on exposed ends. Always stagger joints on adjacent courses. Chart on page 172 shows the various size and shape blocks available.

*Book #697 Forms, Footings, Foundations, Framing, Stair Building also explains how to use a transit.

49

6. After establishing the number of blocks for first course and exact size of mortar joints, remove blocks. Spread an inch thick layer of mortar about 9″ wide over a 34″ area at each end of one wall, Illus. 61.

7. Drop a plumb bob down from guide line. Allow point of bob to mark concrete at three points, Illus. 61. Draw lines in mortar to indicate corner. Place corner block. Check block with level horizontally and vertically. Do the same at the opposite corner.

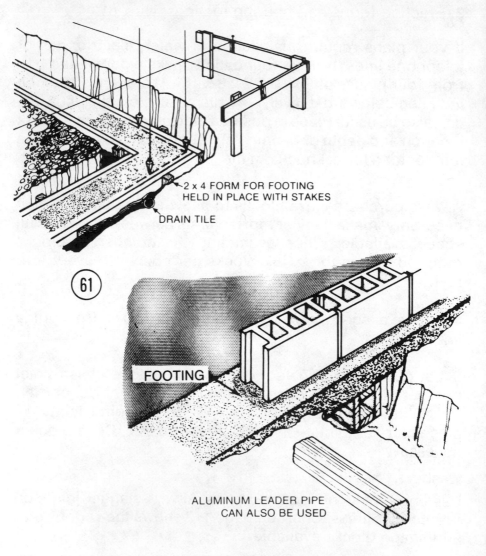

2 x 4 FORM FOR FOOTING
HELD IN PLACE WITH STAKES

DRAIN TILE

(61)

FOOTING

ALUMINUM LEADER PIPE
CAN ALSO BE USED

Stretch a line between corner blocks, Illus. 62.

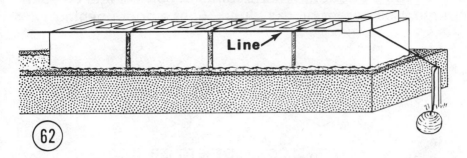

Line

62

Lay each block to the line, Illus. 63. Continually check each course with a level, horizontally as well as vertically. Check each corner with a square.

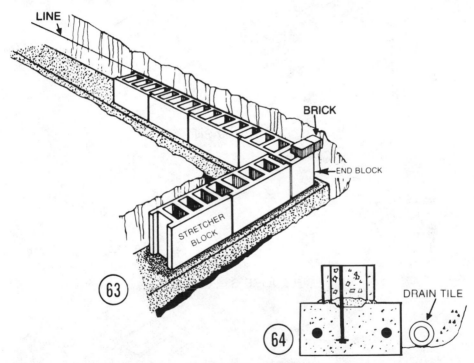

LINE

BRICK

END BLOCK

STRETCHER BLOCK

63

DRAIN TILE

64

If building codes or high wind conditions warrant anchoring first course of block to the footing, embed 12 or 15" bolts and washers, Illus. 64, in footing in position cores in block permit. Space anchor bolts every 8'. Allow bolts to project 7" above footing. Anchor these bolts to blocks by filling cores in first course.

Lay blocks along the first course, corner to corner, or corner to a window or door. Overlap joints at corners and on each course. Use corner blocks, Illus. 65, at a door opening.

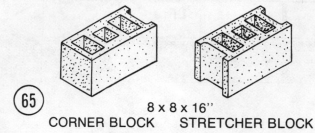

(65)

8 x 8 x 16"
CORNER BLOCK   STRETCHER BLOCK

Use channel blocks, Illus. 66, for a steel or aluminum window. Use blocks noted for a wood sash, Illus. 67.

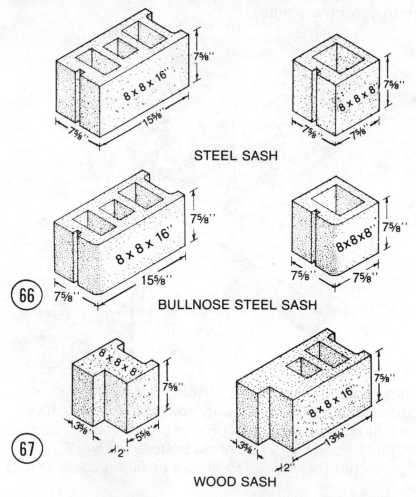

STEEL SASH

(66)

BULLNOSE STEEL SASH

(67)

WOOD SASH

Always allow for an expansion joint in a long or high wall, Illus. 68. These relieve contraction. This is especially important on walls over 30' in length.

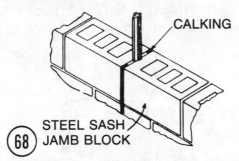

CALKING

STEEL SASH
68 JAMB BLOCK

One method of relieving pressure is to position steel sash blocks in a vertical line, Illus. 68. These accommodate a preformed rubber control joint, Illus. 69. Install a control joint where building specification and/or code require.

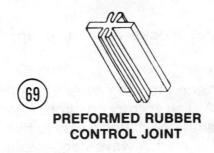

69

**PREFORMED RUBBER
CONTROL JOINT**

The wood sash block, Illus. 67, can also be used as an expansion joint, Illus. 70. Allow ½" or gap height and/or length of wall require. Fill gap with calking, Illus. 68.

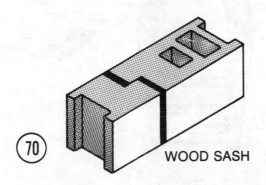

70

WOOD SASH

Use a chisel to cut a block. Draw a line clear around block. Place block on a bag of sand, Illus. 71, placed over a level area. Make cuts an even depth all along drawn line rather than attempt to cut through. Strike chisel with hammer. Apply same pressure as you move chisel along drawn line.

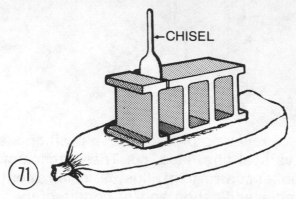

←CHISEL

71

Stagger joints so cut blocks never line up on adjacent courses.

After spreading mortar on footing, Illus. 61, butter up end of each block, Illus. 72. Tap it into position. Keep all mortar joints to thickness estimated. If necessary to fill space, a ½ or ¾'' mortar joint can be used. Always stagger joints as shown, Illus. 73.

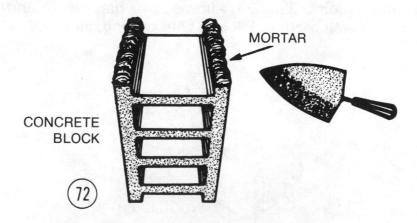

MORTAR

CONCRETE
BLOCK

72

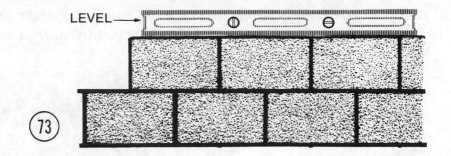

LEVEL →

(73)

Tap each block into position. Never move a block after concrete begins to set.

A course of block can be laid completely around footings, or you can build up to a height required, Illus. 74. Always position a taut, level guide line from corner to corner. Move this when starting each course.

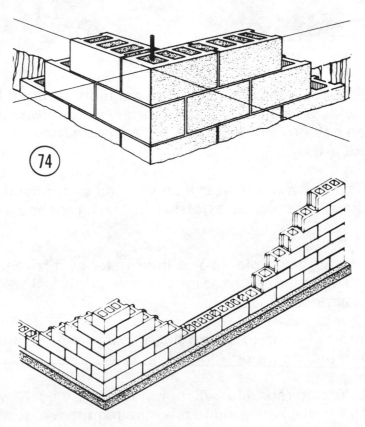

(74)

Using a trowel, cut surplus mortar away from joint and throw it back onto mortar board, Illus. 75. Always turn mortar with your trowel so no small globs harden.

(75)

Use a ⅝ or ¾" piece of plywood as a mortar board. Paint board with oil before placing mortar. Hose down board between batches and paint with oil. A wheelbarrow can also be used.

Never mix any more mortar than you can conveniently use within 2 to 2½ hours. On a hot day, add water to keep mortar plastic.

When mixing concrete, use as little water as mix requires. When mixing mortar, use as much water as mix will take and still remain plastic.

Allow mortar joints to set up finger print hard, then finish joint with a concave or V jointer, Illus. 47.

Use reinforcing rods, Illus. 76, or welded wire, Illus. 77, when building a wall where ground pressure requires same. When laying rods, overlap ends. When building concrete block walls above grade, reinforcing every other course with rods or wire is highly recommended, particularly in areas subject to high winds. Embed reinforcing completely within mortar joint.

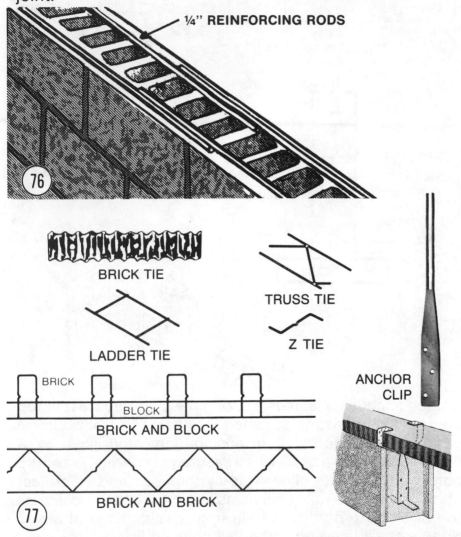

¼" **REINFORCING RODS**

76

BRICK TIE

TRUSS TIE

Z TIE

LADDER TIE

ANCHOR CLIP

BRICK

BLOCK

BRICK AND BLOCK

BRICK AND BRICK

77

When building a concrete block wall that is to be faced with brick, use 10 x 8 x 16" blocks below grade, Illus. 78, then 6 x 8 x 16" blocks from grade level up. This allows a shoulder for brick facing. Embed brick ties, Illus. 77, in position chart, Illus. 79, recommends.

BRICK VENEER TIE SPACING

DESIGN WIND LOAD psf	SPACING HORIZONTAL BY VERTICAL IN.	WALL AREA per TIE. sq.ft.
20	24 by 24	4
30	16 by 24	2-2/3
40	16 by 28	2

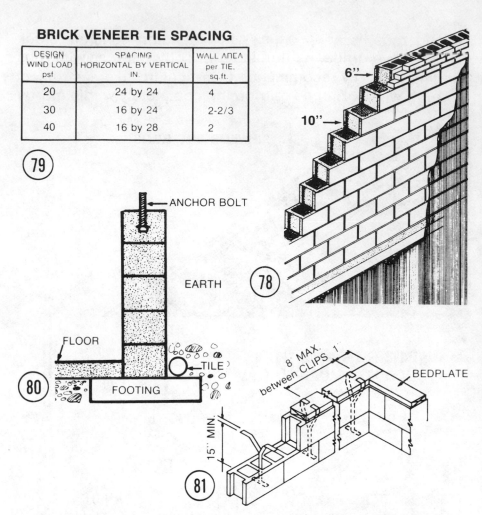

Embed anchor bolts, Illus. 80, or plate clips, Illus. 81, in top course. Most masons set anchor bolts 4'' in from outside edge of foundation wall, in position indicated, Illus. 74. A washer at head of a bolt locks it securely in conrete. Fill entire core with concrete allowing only threaded end to project about 4'' above block. Drill holes in 2 x 4's. Lay these across top of block to hold bolt 4'' in from outside edge of block. Snap a chalk line and embed all bolts on line.

The clips provide a better way to anchor starting course of block to footing; or a bedplate to concrete block foundation. This method of construction is recommended in areas subject to high winds.

WINDOW INSTALLATION — BLOCK WALL

Due to the wide variation in design and size of steel, aluminum and wood windows, it's important to follow directions window manufacturer specifies concerning size of opening, framing, nailing, or use of anchoring fasteners. Always allow exact amount of space manufacturer recommends for calking and flashing.

Those installing a window or door in a block wall must build the wall up to height of lintel over window, Illus. 82,83.

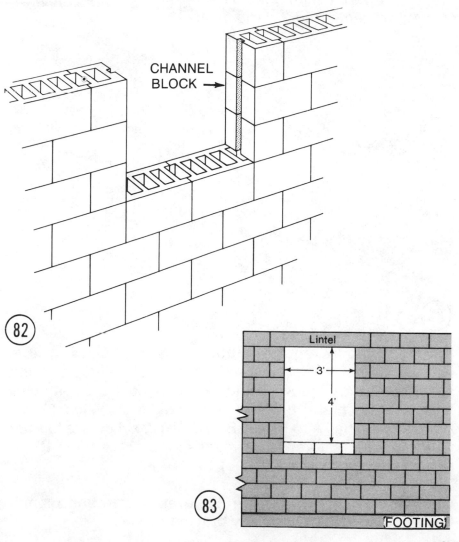

CHANNEL BLOCK →

82

Lintel

3'

4'

83

FOOTING

Channel blocks, Illus. 66, designed to receive a steel or aluminum sash, are positioned where window requires same, Illus. 82.

Where block is exposed in space used for living, use bullnose sash blocks, Illus. 66.

Slide windows down from the top. Temporarily support at height required using a piece of brick, stone or block. Insert putty, wedges or fastening manufacturer of window recommends. Trowel a sill in place. Bevel sill to outside, Illus. 84. Use 1 part cement to 2 parts sand.

Where a window requires a buck, Illus. 85, build it to size window manufacturer suggests. A buck simplifies pouring sill after setting window in place. Position buck in opening so it finishes flush at top with a course of blocks, Illus. 86. To build a buck, nail A to B. Nail B to C. Use 2 x 4 or size lumber window manufacturer recommends for C. Drive some 1'' big head nails into side and top of C.

Check buck to make certain it's level, square and plumb. Hold in place with temporary bracing.

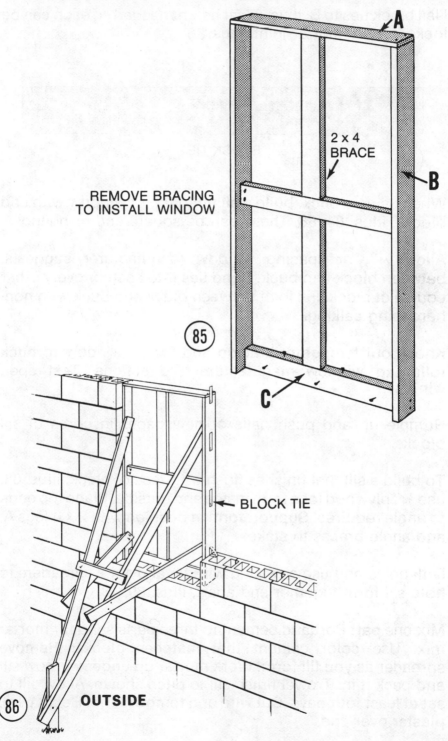

**REMOVE BRACING
TO INSTALL WINDOW**

2 x 4
BRACE

A

B

C

⑧⑤

BLOCK TIE

⑧⑥   **OUTSIDE**

61

Nail block ties to B, Illus. 87, at height needed so each can be locked into a mortar joint, Illus. 86.

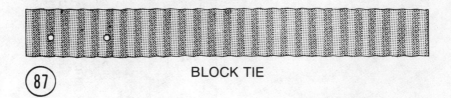

(87) BLOCK TIE

When using a buck, build wall up to top of window with end blocks, Illus. 84, 86. These can be square end or bullnose.

Allow ¼", or spacing window manufacturer suggests, between block and buck. Bend ties into each or every other course of block. Fill joint between block and buck with non-hardening calking.

Knock out temporary bracing and fasten window to buck following window manufacturer's directions. Test open window.

Rumple up and push balls of newspaper in cores of sill blocks.

To build a sill that finishes flush with face of block, Illus. 88, use ¾" plywood for a form inside and outside. Plane top edge to angle required. Support form in position with 2 x 4 legs A, and angle braces to stakes.

Drill holes and use a twisted wire tie and 1 x 2 spreaders to hold sill form together and apart, Illus. 89.

Mix one part Portland cement to three parts sand for mortar mix. Use color cement that matches blocks. Remove spreader as you fill form. Work mortar up under window sill and pack it in. Trowel finish sill to pitch shown. Allow sill to set at least four days. Cut wire and remove form. Recut wire, plaster over end.

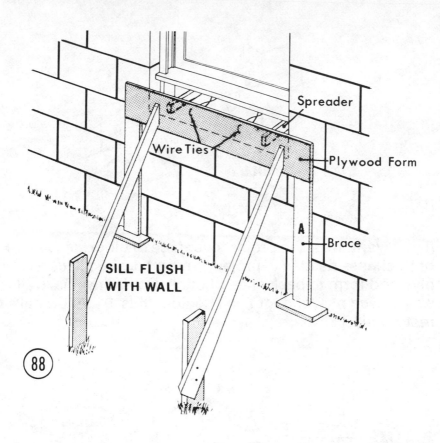

Spreader

Wire Ties

Plywood Form

A ·—Brace

**SILL FLUSH
WITH WALL**

(88)

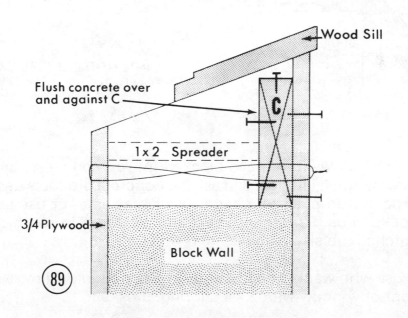

Wood Sill

Flush concrete over
and against C

C

1 x 2 Spreader

3/4 Plywood ——►

Block Wall

(89)

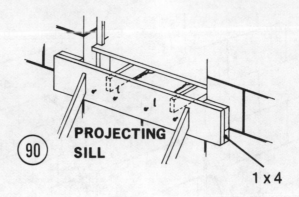

90 **PROJECTING SILL**

1 x 4

If you want the sill to project over face of block, place a 1 x 4 or thickness needed to project amount desired, Illus. 90. Nail plywood form to back edge of buck. Don't drive nails all the way. Brace plywood form in position, Illus. 91. Allow nails to rest on sill.

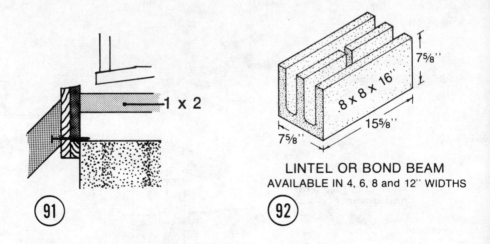

1 x 2

91

7⅝"

8 x 8 x 16"

15⅝"

7⅝"

LINTEL OR BOND BEAM
AVAILABLE IN 4, 6, 8 and 12" WIDTHS

92

After windows have been blocked in, you can either buy a precast lintel, Illus. 83, and ask the concrete products dealer to hoist it in position when he delivers same; or use lintel blocks, Illus. 92. Lintel blocks are available in width that matches the size block used in wall.

Those who want to build a lintel in place should fill recess in front of window with 2 x 4 shoring, Illus. 93.

64

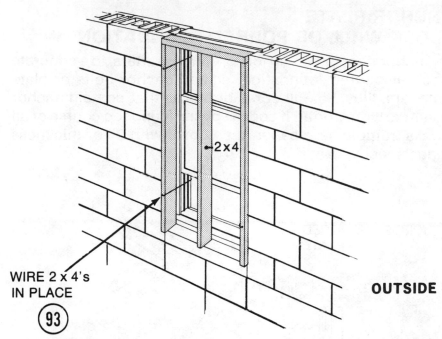

WIRE 2 x 4's
IN PLACE

2 x 4

OUTSIDE

(93)

Place lintel blocks, groove side up, end to end, Illus. 94. Fill grooves with 1'' of concrete. Cut ½'' reinforcing rod full length of assembled blocks and embed same in position. Fill grooves with another 2'' of mortar and embed two more rods. Fill block to top. Allow beam to set undisturbed for four or more days, then complete perimeter course of block.

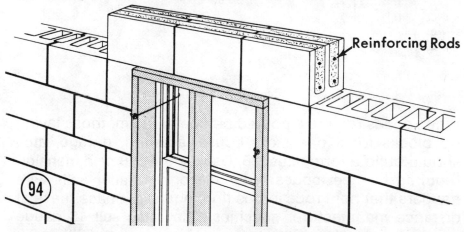

Reinforcing Rods

(94)

Calk joint around windows with calking window manufacturer recommends.

ANCHOR PLATE
BLOCK WALL OR POURED FOUNDATION

To anchor floor or ceiling joists, or truss rafters, to a concrete block or poured foundation, embed anchor bolts or plate fasteners, Illus. 95. Fill cores of blocks that contain anchor fasteners with mortar. If codes specify filling top course of all blocks, rumple newspaper, then cover with 2" or thickness codes specify.

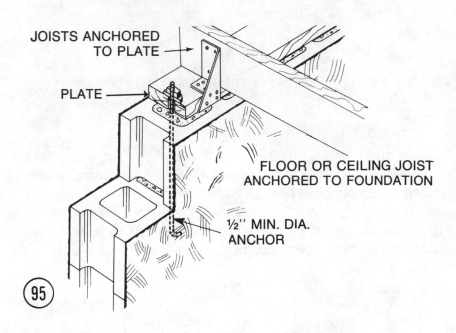

JOISTS ANCHORED TO PLATE

PLATE

FLOOR OR CEILING JOIST ANCHORED TO FOUNDATION

½" MIN. DIA. ANCHOR

95

When codes require a poured perimeter beam, those laying up blocks for a one story house, addition, garage, etc., should build a form, Illus. 96. Use 2 x 6, 2 x 8 or dimension required to meet codes. Your masonry retailer sells wire hangers that hold rods in position required. Space these at distance manufacturer specifies. They also sell 18 gauge galvanized steel ceiling joist or truss anchors, Illus. 97. These, positioned before pouring beam, simplify securing ceiling joists or truss rafters to foundation, Illus. 81.

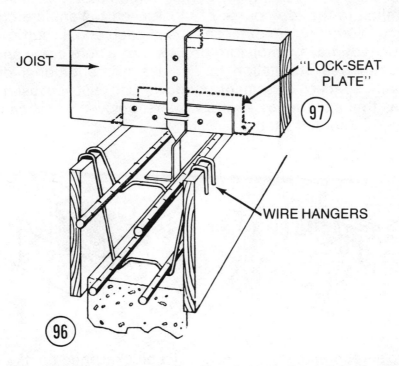

JOIST

"LOCK-SEAT PLATE"

97

WIRE HANGERS

96

Form for poured perimeter beam. Note hangers for reinforcing rods; truss anchors for ceiling or floor joists. These are also used to anchor prefabricated rafters.

CRAWL SPACE VENTILATION

Illus. 98 shows one type of metal ventilator that can be installed in the top course of block used to ventilate crawl space. Normally two of these, one at each end, is sufficient. Where you have a moisture problem, or where crawl space requires free circulation of air, use two additional ones equally spaced. Basement windows can also be used. In areas that experience severe winters, buy vents that can be closed in cold weather.

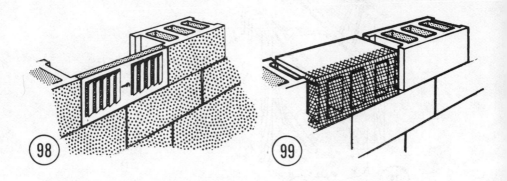

Wire screening bent over edge of a block turned on its side, Illus. 99, can also be used as a vent. Use fine wire mesh to discourage bees.

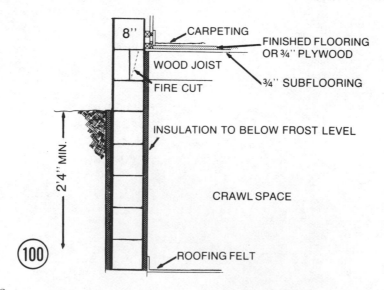

Always insulate crawl space under a house, Illus. 100.

Insulation applied to outside of foundation should be covered with asbestos cement board, or other protective weatherproof panelboard.

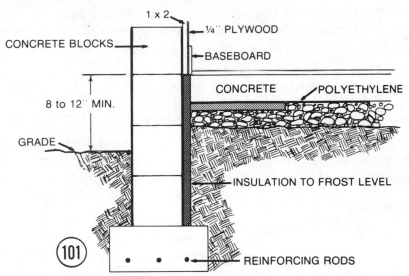

1 x 2
¼" PLYWOOD
CONCRETE BLOCKS
BASEBOARD
CONCRETE
POLYETHYLENE
8 to 12" MIN.
GRADE
INSULATION TO FROST LEVEL
(101)
REINFORCING RODS

Rigid foam insulation keeps out cold. It also acts as a compression joint between slab and foundation, Illus. 101. This is especially important where you are pouring a slab on grade. Use mastic insulation manufacturer recommends. Protect insulation with asbestos cement board, Illus. 102. Cover edge with a strip of flashing, Illus. 54.

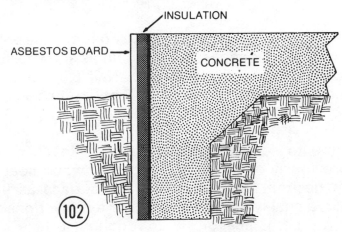

INSULATION
ASBESTOS BOARD
CONCRETE
(102)

WALKS

Walks are usually laid 36 to 48" wide, 1½ to 3½" thick, over at least 3" of crushed stone or gravel. Slope walk away from house ⅛ to ¼" per foot.

Cut strips of asphalt impregnated insulation board, 1" less than thickness of slab. Place these every 4 or 6 feet as control joints. Finish joint with a groover, Illus. 25.

Forms can be built as shown, Illus. 103. Pour concrete in alternate sections. After sections set, remove end forms (don't disturb expansion joint) and pour intermediate sections. Screed concrete flush with top of form using a straight 2 x 4 as a screed. Work this back and forth, saw fashion.

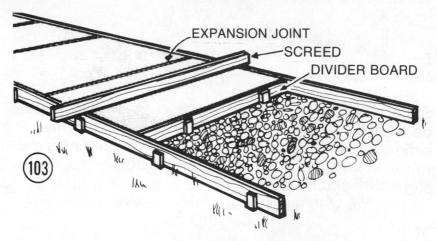

EXPANSION JOINT
SCREED
DIVIDER BOARD

103

A self-aligning screed that keeps working concrete to center of form, instead of over edges, may be built as shown, Illus. 104. Bolt two 1 x 4 by length needed. Nail 3" blocks in position indicated. Spread concrete by working this screed back and forth.

Allow concrete to set until stiff enough to float. Follow directions previously outlined. Use a steel or wood float to obtain finish desired. Don't overwork the surface as this tends to make a chalky, dusty surface. For a gritty, nonskid surface, use a broom, Illus. 37, 38, to roughen surface.

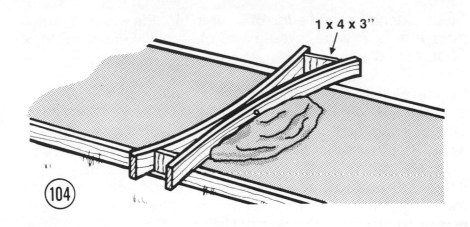

1 x 4 x 3"

(104)

BUILDING STEPS

Use lumber free of knots, smooth on one side. Keep smooth side in. Brace forms with stakes to prevent buckling. Excavate area for steps to depth below frost level. Fill with stone and gravel.

Since risers can be 7 or 8" in height, measure distance from door sill to grade level. Divide this distance by 7" (or 8") to estimate number of steps or risers, Illus. 105. Build platform to height required to provide space for needed number of steps. Check with level.

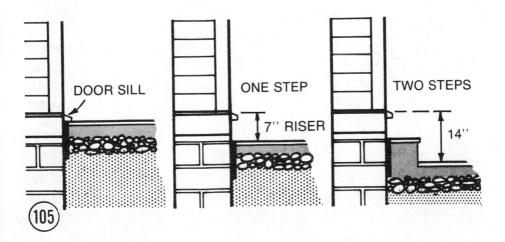

DOOR SILL

ONE STEP

7" RISER

TWO STEPS

14"

(105)

Steps extend beyond edge of door to include width of trim. If door trim is 4'' wide, overall size of step will equal width of door, plus 8''.

Measure steps you find acceptable, build yours same size.

The starting platform should measure an additional 12'' wide. Step treads can be 8'' wide when overall distance X, Illus. 106, is 6'0'' or less; 10'' wide when X measures up to 8'0''. The starting platform should be constructed to height required. Drive stakes firmly into ground. Nail stakes to B but do not drive nails all the way in. The top edge of platform form should be distance down from bottom of door to allow for number of steps required. Use 1 x 8 for a 7¼'' riser. Use 2 x 8 x 8 or longer for forms. Use 1 x 4 for cross ties to prevent forms from buckling. To permit finishing steps under riser, Illus. 107, bevel bottom edge to angle shown, Illus. 108.

Build form for platform, Illus. 106, to height above grade needed for one, two or more steps. Excavate to depth required to position platform flush with grade, or at height desired.

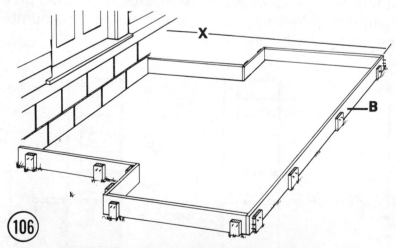

First pour platform. Allow to set 3 days then pour steps.

Drive stakes to hold forms. If stakes are driven flush with top edge of form, they don't interfere when you screed concrete.

Build form for steps using 1 x 8 or ⅝'' plywood. Cut to overall size required, Illus. 107. Measure 7'' down for one step, 14'' down for two steps. Pour concrete for steps in one pouring. Work concrete down with beveled 1 x 4 or pointed 2 x 4. Use mix specified, Illus. 1.

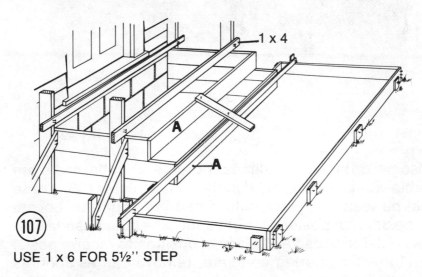

USE 1 x 6 FOR 5½'' STEP

Cut both ends off a beer can, C, Illus. 108. Grease outside face and place in position needed for leg on iron railings.

IRON RAILING REPAIR, INSTALLATION

Handsome ornamental railings, porch and patio posts are available at your building supply center, Illus. 109. These should be tested in place before pouring concrete. Locate exact position of posts. Cut both ends off a beer or soda can. Grease outside of can and place in position to receive posts, Illus. 110. After pouring concrete, remove can as soon as concrete permits.

After concrete has been allowed to set (three or more days), brace ironwork in plumb position. Anchor post using melted lead or the plug sealant mentioned on page 48.

If a leg on iron railing has rusted out, hacksaw leg close to railing. Leave sufficient stud above concrete to grasp with pliers. Use a propane torch, Illus. 111, to heat lead. Use pliers to remove embedded piece. Plug cement sealants or hot lead can be used to anchor new support.

In many cases a piece of 3/16 x 1'' strap steel, bent to shape shown, Illus. 112, drilled with holes indicated, can be embedded in lead or plug sealant. Drill holes in lower rail to match those in new leg. Bolt leg to rail, Illus. 113.

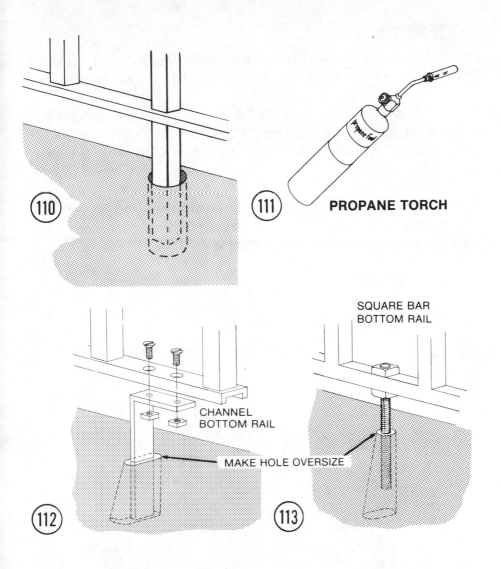

⑩

⑪ **PROPANE TORCH**

SQUARE BAR
BOTTOM RAIL

CHANNEL
BOTTOM RAIL

MAKE HOLE OVERSIZE

⑫

⑬

Where an existing leg can't easily be removed, drill through bottom rail with a 5/16, ⅜ or ½'' bit. After drilling hole through rail, use a carbon tipped bit to drill a hole in concrete. Insert a threaded steel rod through rail, thread a nut on rod. Drive rod into hole. Fasten rod in hole with lead. When lead sets, snug up nut to bottom of rail. Place another nut, Illus. 113, in position shown. Cut surplus rod with a hacksaw.

STEP REPAIR

Repairing cracked and broken concrete steps is no big deal. It does take a bit of time to build a form to fit the curve of step.

To shape a rounded edge, cut a piece of ⅛" hardboard to exact shape. First cut a paper or cardboard pattern. When it fits, trace on hardboard. Fasten hardboard to a 1 x 2 form, Illus. 114.

Cut 1 x 4 or 1 x 6 A and B to exact width required, Illus. 115. Use a concrete block to hold these in position. Mix mortar so it holds its shape. Apply and shape mortar with form.

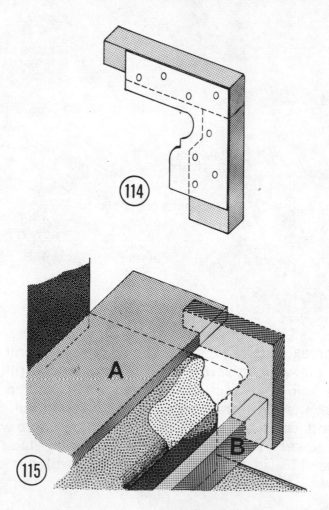

HOW TO INSTALL BASEMENT ENTRY DOOR

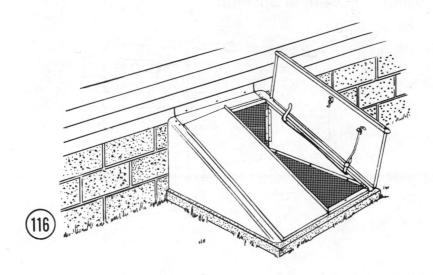

As the weather map changes and tornadoes devastate wide areas, having easy access to a basement can prove a life saver. Select a location that's readily accessible and won't interfere with future plans for a garage, patio, etc. Since you may want to store bulky pieces, carry in panels of plywood, etc., use thought in selecting a site. We recommend installation of a 3'0" x 6'8" door in basement, Illus. 117.

Double check location selected to make certain no sewer, gas or water line will be disturbed. Don't select a site near a septic tank or field.

If your basement has a window, consider removing and cutting door through. Don't cut an opening closer than 2'10" to an existing window.

After selecting a location, ask your building material retailer for overall size of opening for a basement entry door. He can advise concerning overall size of excavation, foundation, and size of rough opening. Excavate to depth equal to bottom of house footing.

Working inside, draw a line to indicate center of proposed opening. Draw lines equal distance from center line, Illus 117, to indicate width of opening.

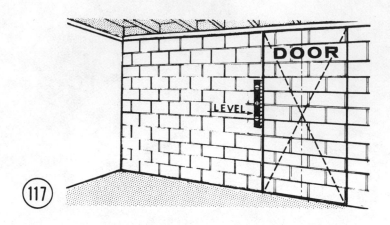

Go outside and stake out site of excavation, Illus. 118.

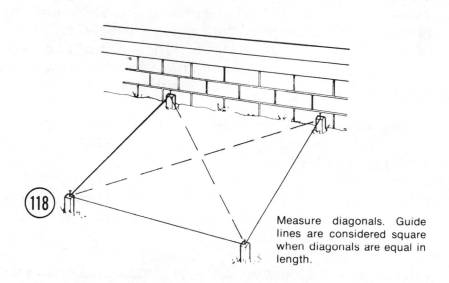

Measure diagonals. Guide lines are considered square when diagonals are equal in length.

Cut opening to width of door plus 5½". This allows for 2 x 6 or 2 x 8 frame.

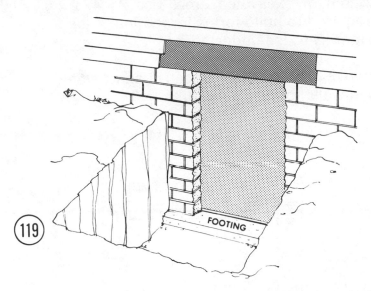

119

Excavate to depth of footing, Illus. 119. If a prefab stair stringer is to be installed, excavate to provide space manufacturer specifies. If you build your own stairs, slope hole as shown, Illus. 120.

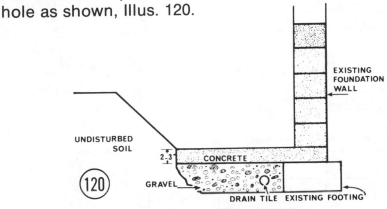

EXISTING
FOUNDATION
WALL

UNDISTURBED
SOIL

2-3"

CONCRETE

120

GRAVEL

DRAIN TILE   EXISTING FOOTING

Concrete blocks can be broken with a bricklayer's chisel and hammer, Illus. 71. Start at center of line and work out. Chip blocks out 5½'' beyond edge of door. Chop blocks down to existing footing.

If you rent an electric hammer, use bit dealer recommends. Be sure to wear safety goggles when using a chisel or electric hammer.

79

Level bottom of excavated area. Use 2 x 4, 2 x 6 or size lumber required to build forms for footing. Keep footings at same height as those under house.

Place drain in position where it can channel water into a dry well. Build walls to height required.

If you prefer concrete block steps, Illus. 121, use 8 x 8 x 16 or 8 x 10 x 16''.

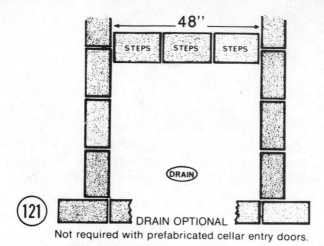

(121) DRAIN OPTIONAL
Not required with prefabricated cellar entry doors.

Back wall of excavation can be sloped as shown, Illus. 122. Cover undisturbed soil with 2'' of gravel, and set blocks in a thick bed of mortar.

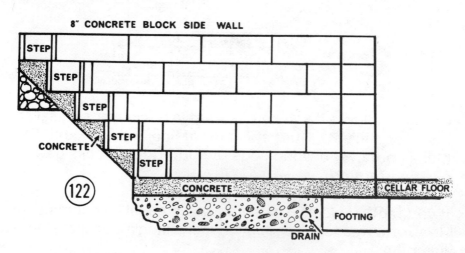

8" CONCRETE BLOCK SIDE WALL

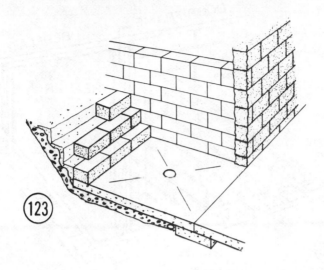

Allow each step to overlap step below 1", Illus. 123.

If you want to pour concrete steps, Illus. 124, build forms as previously described.

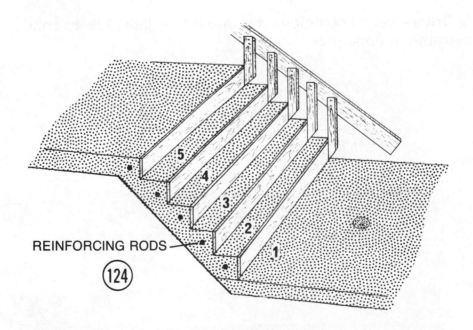

REINFORCING RODS

Lay floor of entry an inch lower than floor in cellar. Slope floor to drain.

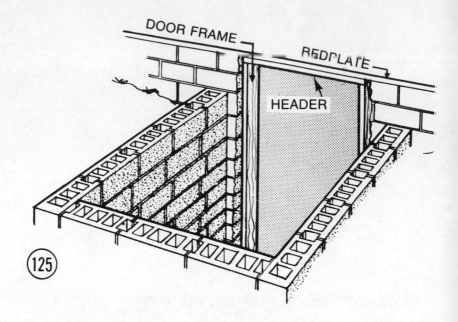

DOOR FRAME

BEDPLATE

HEADER

(125)

Build door frame, Illus. 125, using same size lumber as existing bedplate, to overall size door requires.

Drive 8 penny common nails into frame, Illus. 126, to anchor frame in concrete.

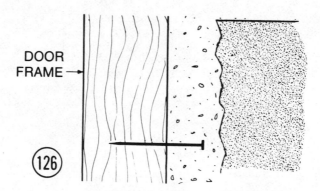

DOOR FRAME →

(126)

Set frame in place, flush with inside face of wall. Check with level and brace in position, Illus. 127.

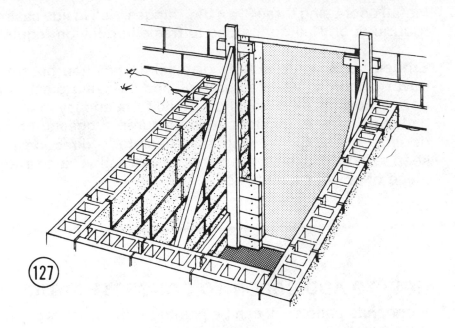

(127)

Tack bracing, inside and out, to hold frame plumb and level against block wall. Nail through header to bedplate. If header doesn't butt against bedplate, cut 2 x 4 filler blocks to length required and nail to header and bedplate.

If two floor joists are nailed together within area cut for door, use a double header over door. Use two 2 x 4 studs between header and bedplate. Place 2 x 4 studs under bedplate, in line with floor joists.

Wet edge of block and footing adjacent to door frame. Paint broken blocks and footing with a wet mixture; 1 part cement to 2 parts sand.

Temporarily nail short pieces of 1 x 6 to inside and outside of door frame, Illus. 127. Brace other end against block. Fill form with 1:2½:3 concrete mix. Tap 1 x 6 to settle concrete. Use a stick to make certain concrete fills all pockets. Add 1 x 6's as you work your way up. Use a stiff concrete mix when you get to top. When concrete begins to harden sufficiently, remove forms and plaster surface.

Install door using three 3½ x 3½" hinges. Nail inside casings around door. Nail door stops to frame in position required.

Embed bolts in top course of block in position basement cover requires. Manufacturer of prefabricated steel entry doors provides exact location. Build form and lay mortar to cap blocks as entry door manufacturer suggests. Fasten door to housing following manufacturer's directions. To keep rain out of excavation during construction, keep a large piece of polyethylene handy.

HOW TO ADD COLOR TO CONCRETE PATIO

A concrete patio deck can be painted with masonry paint or dye. Your building supply retailer offers a wide selection of colors.

The best time to add color is when you are laying concrete. Do this in two courses. First mix color selected with white Portland cement. Mix in proportion to manufacturer's recommendations. Do not add water; keep dry.

Lay first course of concrete to within ½ to 1" from top of form. Add dry sand to your color mix in proportion recommended, mix well. When thoroughly blended, add water. Spread and level color course following procedure outlined. Color can be used full strength. Pastel shades are achieved when less color is used in proportion to a bag of white cement.

PAVE A PATIO

(128)

A colored concrete patio, Illus. 128, can provide a lot of enjoyable living space. Many different designs can be achieved using a groover, Illus. 25.

Directions explain laying a 9 x 12' patio, Illus. 129. Alter size to fill your needs.

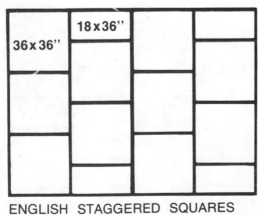

36x36"

18x36"

(129) ENGLISH STAGGERED SQUARES

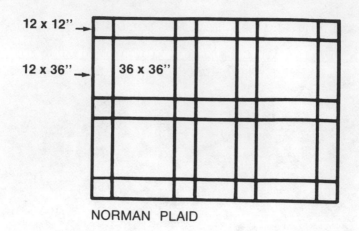

NORMAN PLAID

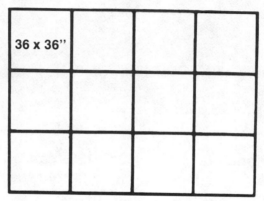

SURREY SQUARES

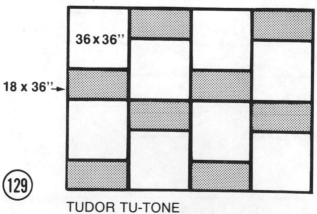

TUDOR TU-TONE

86

If patio is laid alongside an outside door, its finished height should not be more than 8'' from door sill, Illus. 130.

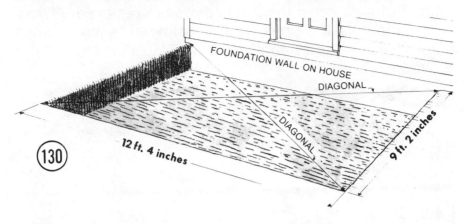

FOUNDATION WALL ON HOUSE

DIAGONAL

DIAGONAL

12 ft. 4 inches

9 ft. 2 inches

(130)

Construction of three different patios is explained. One is a 3½'' slab, Illus. 128, on grade.

The second uses ¼ x 1 x 6 or 8' lengths of aluminum as dividers, Illus. 131. These remain embedded in slab and around outside edge when 2 x 4 forms are removed.

8 PENNY ALUMINUM NAIL

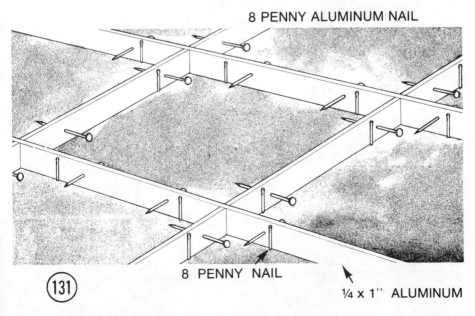

(131)

8 PENNY NAIL

¼ x 1'' ALUMINUM

87

The third uses 1 x 4 redwood as both dividers and forms, Illus. 132. These remain embedded in slab and around outside of slab when the 2 x 4 forms are removed. Always check diagonals. Forms are considered square when diagonals are equal in length. Cut a half lap joint, Illus. 133, in redwood.

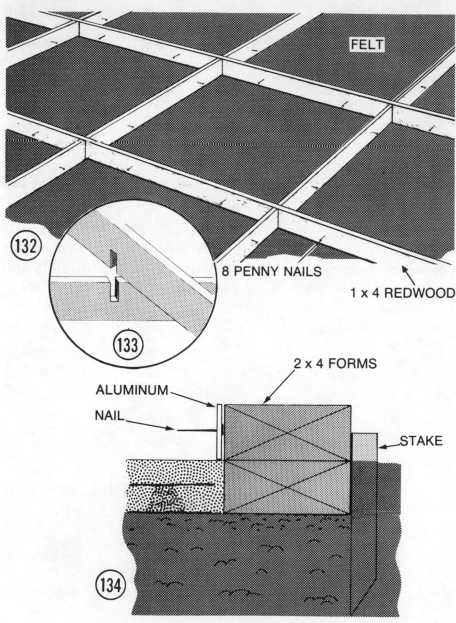

FELT

(132)

8 PENNY NAILS

1 x 4 REDWOOD

(133)

2 x 4 FORMS

ALUMINUM

NAIL

STAKE

(134)

Always pitch dividers and forms ⅛" per foot away from house. The low edge of a 9'0" wide patio will be 1⅛" lower than point butting house.

Always plan low point of slab to finish at least 1" above grade.

To lock the outside aluminum or redwood divider to slab, place nails through divider, Illus. 134, butting against form. Do not drive nails into form.

In cold climes excavate area to below frost level. Fill with fieldstone, then at least a total of 3" of 1½ and ¾" gravel, Illus. 135. Compact gravel.

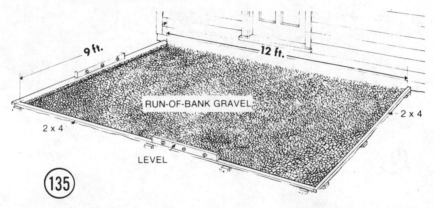

Position expansion strip, Illus. 136, alongside house. This can be 6" in width or width equal to slab. Paint forms with old crankcase oil before staking in position.

If patio is to be totally enclosed and used for living space, spread a polyethylene vapor barrier over gravel after compacting, Illus. 136.

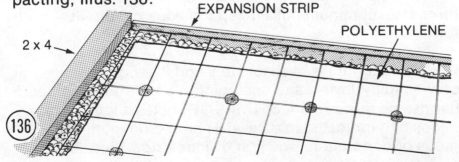

Place expansion strip alongside house. Paint 2 x 4 forms with old crankcase oil and place in position. Keep inside dimension of form 9'0" x 12'0" or size desired. Use stakes to hold forms in position. Be sure to slope form to pitch desired. Backfill form to keep it from losing concrete.

For those embedding ¼ x 1 x 8' aluminum dividers, place 2 x 4 forms flatwise. Pour a sub slab 1½". Embed reinforcing in sub slab. Screed slab. Before it begins to set, score, Illus. 137. Use 1:2¼:3 mixture for sub slab.

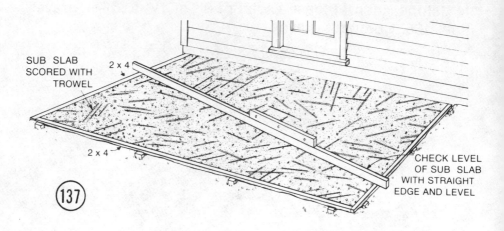

SUB SLAB SCORED WITH TROWEL

2 x 4

2 x 4

CHECK LEVEL OF SUB SLAB WITH STRAIGHT EDGE AND LEVEL

137

Next lay 2 x 4 outside forms flatwise for finishing slab. Position aluminum divider to pattern desired, Illus. 129, 138.

The aluminum divider strip, butting expansion joint, can be held in place by nailing to expansion joint, but not to 2 x 4 form. Use aluminum nails. Keep top edge of strip flush with form.

¼ x 1" aluminum is available in 6 and 8' lengths. These not only simplify laying and screeding a patio, but also add a handsome terrazzo effect. Drill 9/16" holes about 12" apart, in position indicated to receive 8 penny aluminum nails. Use globs of concrete to position divider strips, Illus. 139.

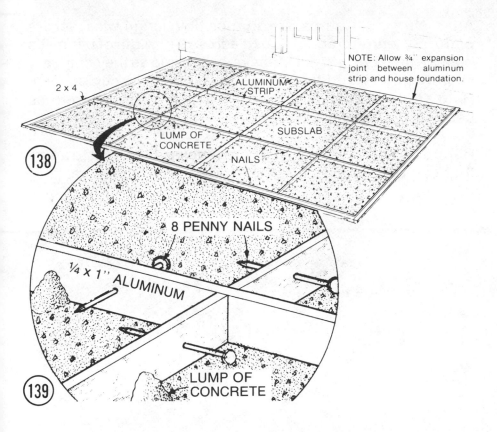

2 x 4

ALUMINUM STRIP

NOTE: Allow ¾" expansion joint between aluminum strip and house foundation.

SUBSLAB

LUMP OF CONCRETE

NAILS

(138)

8 PENNY NAILS

¼ X 1" ALUMINUM

(139) LUMP OF CONCRETE

Insert 8 penny aluminum nails through interior dividers. Allow nails to project equal distance from both faces. Place nails through dividers butting against 2 x 4 forms. The nails lock divider to slab, Illus. 134.

Use globs of concrete to level dividers flush with form.

To create a colorful patio, add color selected to white Portland cement. Test various shades to select a color everyone likes. In a test patio, we used "Desert Tan." Although directions on bag recommended adding three parts sand to one of cement, two or two and one half parts of sand to one part cement makes a "neat" mixture which provides a smoother finish. DO NOT use salt beach sand as the salt in the sand kills the color. Mix color with cement before adding sand.

After aluminum strips are in position lengthwise across patio, cut lengths required to fit across 9 ft. width of patio. It's best to measure and cut strips one at a time as they may vary slightly in length. Place strips on edge, correctly spaced. Hold strips in correct position with lumps of concrete as described previously.

Before pouring a section, cut wire fencing, Illus. 140, to a size that can be placed at least 1½'' away from aluminum.

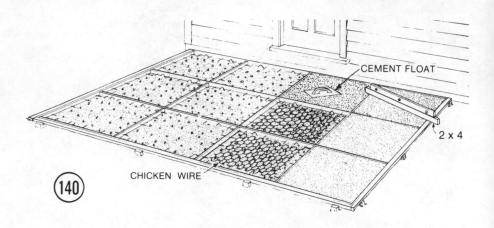

CEMENT FLOAT

2 x 4

(140) CHICKEN WIRE

When positioning aluminum, make certain each is square, slopes desired pitch, and is even with top edge of 2 x 4 form. Check with a taut string stretched across top edge of form.

Pour two sections at a time. Spread, tamp into corners, and screed. Finish each section level with edge of aluminum strip. Work a 1 x 4 x 4' straight edge across aluminum strips to level, Illus. 140. Float rough with a wood float. Float smooth with a steel float. If the concrete is on the dry side, you can begin to float each section almost immediately.

Lay 2 x 4's across and cover with polyethylene, #15 felt or building paper, Illus. 141. This will protect patio from sun while curing. Remove covering paper and spray once or twice a day to help cure properly.

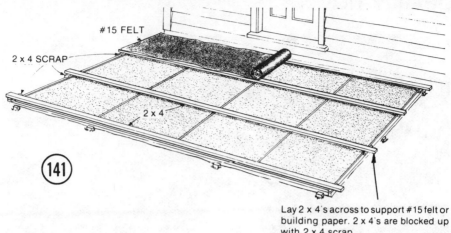

#15 FELT

2 x 4 SCRAP

2 x 4

(141)

Lay 2 x 4's across to support #15 felt or
building paper. 2 x 4's are blocked up
with 2 x 4 scrap.

After concrete has set thoroughly, remove 2 x 4 forms, Illus.
142. Polish top edge of aluminum strips with a fine steel wool.
Back fill around exposed edges.

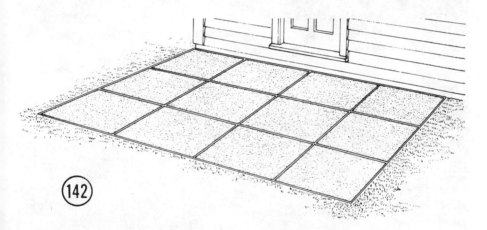

(142)

To give patio a glossy and water shedding finish, apply a coat
of liquid floor wax. Polish with an electric waxer. Repeat
polishing with a second coat of wax two days later.

If you prefer covering slab with slate, flagstone or paver tile,
score slab before concrete has a chance to set, Illus. 137. Or
add color to concrete, score lines in slab, Illus. 142, using
groover, Illus. 25.

QUARRY TILE

For those who want the best, 6 x 6" quarry or paver tile, Illus. 143, 144, is the ultimate. Since it increases the value of your home far more than the tile costs, it generates a sizeable Capital Gains. To estimate spacing, place one row the full length and width of area to be covered. Select the size joint that lessens a need to cut tile.

(144)

Make a layout stick. Mark position of each tile with exact joint spacing.

Set tiles in mortar. You can use #759 Dry Set Mortar. Just add water. A 50 lb. bag will cover approximately 85 to 90 sq.ft. Use the notched trowel, Illus. 145, tile retailer suggests. Sanded ceramic tile cement can be applied up to ¼" thick in one coat. Additional ¼" coats can be added providing you allow each coat to cure time manufacturer specifies.

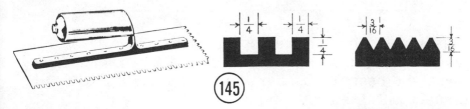

(145)

Using the flat edge of the trowel, first apply a skim coat with pressure. This insures making a good bond. Immediately apply a heavier coat so the finished bed is thickness tile manufacturer recommends.

Comb the bed immediately with the #3 notched trowel. Place each tile and beat into position. Beating is important as it breaks the skin on the mortar. This increases wetting tile by mortar, also increases the total area of contact by forcing mortar between ribs on tile. Beating must be done immediately before mortar has begun to set. Use a block of 2 x 4 and a wood mallet to beat tile into mortar.

Illus. 146 indicates different size tiles available and area covered with various size joints.

QUARRY TILE COVERAGE CHART

		2¾" x 2¾"	2¾" x 6"	3⅞" x 8"	4" x 4"	6" x 6"	9" x 9"
Number of pieces per square foot		19.05	8.73	4.65	9.00	4.00	1.78
Pieces Required To Lay 100 Square Feet Flat Tile	⅛" Joint	1741	818	443	846	384	173
	¼" Joint	1600	768	424	797	369	168
	⅜" Joint	1475	723	405	752	354	164
*Percentage of Quarry Tile Required To Cover an Area After Allowing for Joints	⅛" Joint	92.0%	93.0%	95.3%	94.0%	96.0%	97.2%
	¼" Joint	84.0	88.0	91.2	88.6	92.0	94.4
	⅜" Joint	77.4	82.8	87.2	83.6	88.5	92.1

(146) *Use this chart when ordering. For example, a 100 sq. ft. floor area will require 96 sq. ft. of 6 x 6'' quarry tile when set with a ⅛'' joint.

When laying quarry or paver tile over a sub-slab, spread a ¾'' minimum to 1¼'' maximum thickness setting bed. Note mix for setting beds, Illus. 147.

HORIZONTAL APPLICATION

Coat	Portland cement	Hydrated lime	Dry Sand	Applied Thickness
Setting Bed	1 part	Up to 1/10	5 or 6 parts	¾'' to 1¼''
Pointing Mortar	1 part	1/5 part	2 parts	depth of joint

(147)

Screed and compact level. Next trowel 1/32'' to 1/16'' thick neat cement paste (cement and water) over bed. Immediately place and beat tile making certain each tile makes overall contact with plastic setting bed.

NOTE: Quarry tile is frequently applied to walls in industrial installations. Book #606 How to Lay Ceramic Tile provides excellent information covering application.

Illus. 148, 149 show various size and shape.

QUARRY TILE
(thickness as indicated)

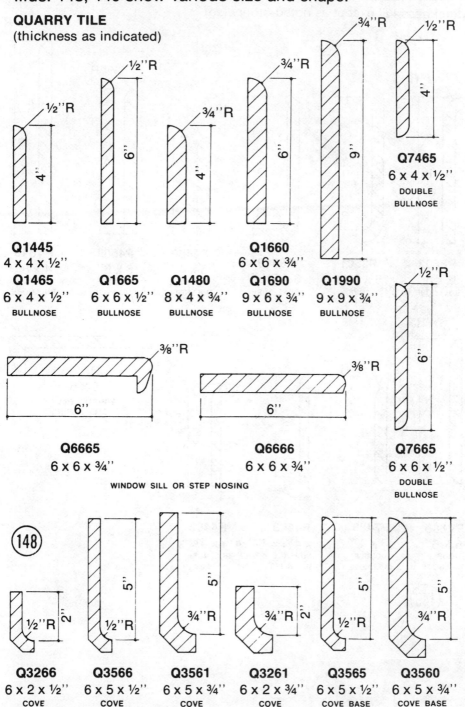

½''R

½''R

¾''R

¾''R

¾''R

½''R

4''

6''

4''

6''

9''

4''

Q7465
6 x 4 x ½''
DOUBLE
BULLNOSE

Q1445
4 x 4 x ½''

Q1660
6 x 6 x ¾''

Q1465
6 x 4 x ½''
BULLNOSE

Q1665
6 x 6 x ½''
BULLNOSE

Q1480
8 x 4 x ¾''
BULLNOSE

Q1690
9 x 6 x ¾''
BULLNOSE

Q1990
9 x 9 x ¾''
BULLNOSE

⅜''R

⅜''R

½''R

6''

6''

6''

Q6665
6 x 6 x ¾''

Q6666
6 x 6 x ¾''

Q7665
6 x 6 x ½''
DOUBLE
BULLNOSE

WINDOW SILL OR STEP NOSING

(148)

5''

5''

5''

5''

½''R

½''R

¾''R

¾''R

½''R

¾''R

2''

2''

Q3266
6 x 2 x ½''
COVE

Q3566
6 x 5 x ½''
COVE

Q3561
6 x 5 x ¾''
COVE

Q3261
6 x 2 x ¾''
COVE

Q3565
6 x 5 x ½''
COVE BASE

Q3560
6 x 5 x ¾''
COVE BASE

PAVER TILE SHAPES AND SIZES

(thickness ½'' except as noted otherwise)

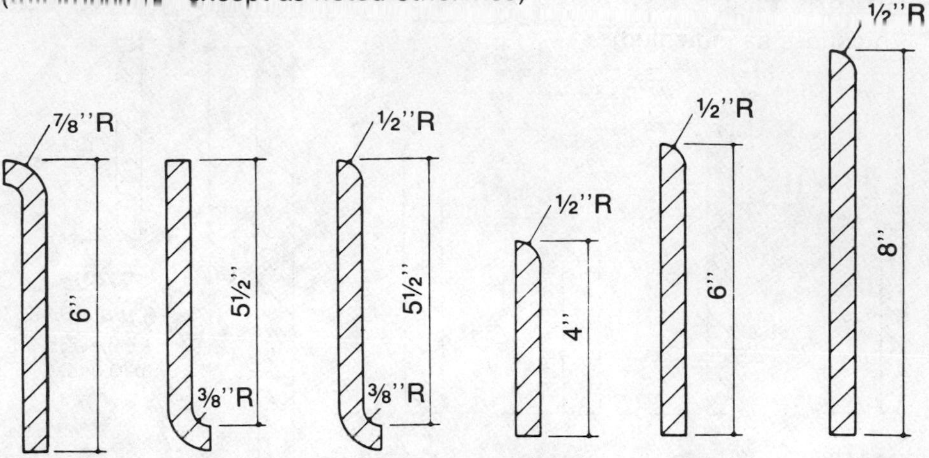

P3602
6 x 6''
BULLNOSE

P3601
6 x 5½''
COVE

P3619
6 x 5½''
COVE BASE

P4489
8 x 4''
SURFACE
BULLNOSE

P4669
6 x 6''
SURFACE
BULLNOSE

P4849
4 x 8''
SURFACE
BULLNOSE

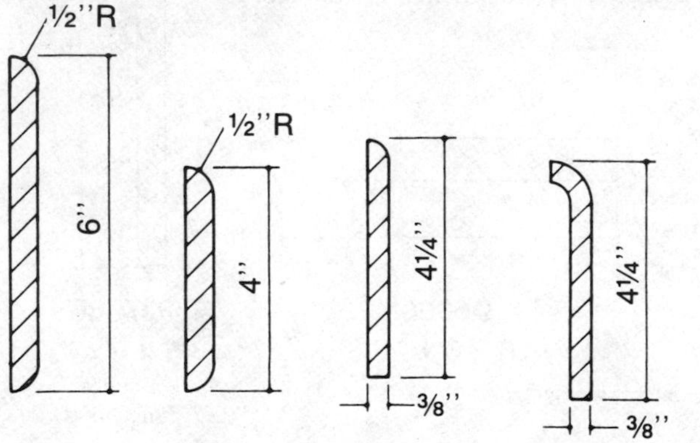

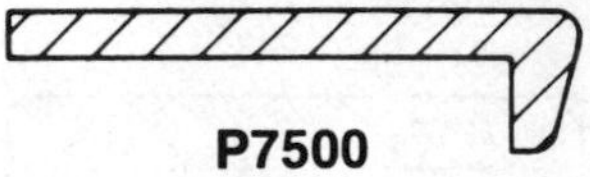

P7669
6 x 6''
DOUBLE
BULLNOSE

P7489
8 x 4''
DOUBLE
BULLNOSE

P4449
4¼ x 4¼ x ⅜''
SURFACE
BULLNOSE

P4402
4¼ x 4¼ x ⅜''
BULLNOSE

P7500
6 x 6''
WINDOW SILL OR
STEP NOSING

149

98

Many tile setters mix 1 part cement, ½ part hydrated lime to 4 parts clean sand, instead of a premix. Add water to make a plastic mix. Spread mortar over area you can conveninently reach. Dust wet mortar with a thin coating of dry cement. Trowel in lightly. Mix a small batch of cement and water to the consistency of thick cream. Paint this cream on back of each tile before pressing in position. Starting at outside corner, place each tile according to layout stick. Beat firmly in mortar. Check with level and straight edge. Keep all tiles square with a straight edge.

After tiles have been allowed to set three or more days, grout joints. Use prepared grout, or mix 1 part white Portland cement to four parts of fine sand. Clean grout off tiles immediately. Finish joints flush or with concave jointer. Wipe tiles clean with water.

When used on steps, porch or entrance hall, paver tiles add a designer's touch to your home. Matching bullnose paver tile can be used to finish edge of tread.

CONCRETE TREE REPAIRS

If you need to perform a major surgical operation on a tree trunk, Illus. 150, consider these steps. Using an adze or curved chisel, remove as much decay as possible. Remove all fungus. Fungus will only continue to destroy the tree. Use special care not to harm the growing layer just under the bark. Protect the edges of the opening by painting with prepared tree paint or shellac. This will keep the edge from drying out.

After removing interior decay, paint the interior with creosote or other solution your nursery recommends for destroying fungus. Do not apply this on the edge of the opening where it can come in contact with the growing cells under the bark.

If you need to treat a large area, after applying creosote, apply a thick coating of hot tar. A really thick layer not only acts as a sealant, but also as an expansion joint.

When filling a cavity greater than 6" deep, cut 6 x 6" reinforcing wire to shape of cavity. Position these horizontally, 3" up from bottom, 1" from back of cavity.

Using a fairly dry mix consisting of one part cement to three parts of sand, pack the concrete into bottom of cavity. Fill the cavity 6" at a time. Be sure to tamp it into every crevice. Leave no air holes. Use a wetter mix around reinforcing wire.

To curve the filling to shape of trunk, make a form, Illus. 151. Using a jig or keyhole saw, cut 1 x 8 by length needed to curve of trunk. Nail a 6" wide strip of galvanized metal in position indicated.

Drill holes in board. Tie a length of clothes line to board in position shown, Illus. 151. Tie form in position required.

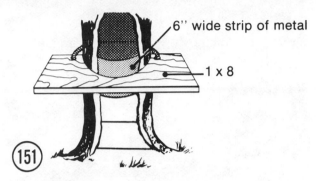

6" wide strip of metal

1 x 8

Pour 6" sections. Shape face to curve of trunk.

Cut a piece of #15 felt and lay on top of each 6" section.

After packing concrete 3" of next 6" section, position reinforcing and continue to fill to 6". Always lay felt over each section. Always cut felt short so it finishes about ½" from front. Use a groover to finish edge of joint.

Always fill cavity to inner edge of growing bark. This allows bark to grow over edge of concrete.

HOW TO BUILD A TREE BENCH

A tree bench, Illus. 152, is a great convenience. Being readily available, it encourages relaxation. Since a tree grows and grows, allow for at least a 10 year period.

(152)

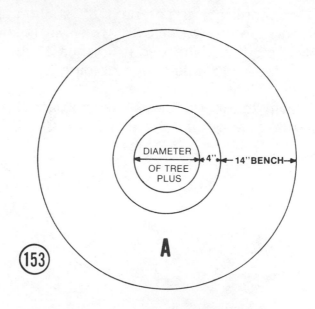

(153)

DIAMETER OF TREE PLUS ◄─4"─► ◄─14" BENCH─►

A

Estimate current diameter. Call your county agent and ask him what the average growth of that species will be per year. Multiply by ten. Add 4" for clearance. Cut A, Illus. 153, to this length.

The following material will be needed.

LIST OF MATERIAL
    1 — 6" x 10' concrete form
    1 — ⅝ or ¾" x 4 x 8' exterior grade plywood
    1 — 2 x 4 x 4'
    1 — 1 x 2 x 4'
    4 — ½ x 6" bolts, nuts and washers
20'— ⅜ x ½" reinforcing rod
36 — 1¼" lag screws
16 — 2" lag screws
Cement, sand, gravel or premix

Plan on building a 14" wide seat. Cut 1 x 2 A, Illus. 154, to length needed. Nail B to A. Use this to draw a circle around tree.

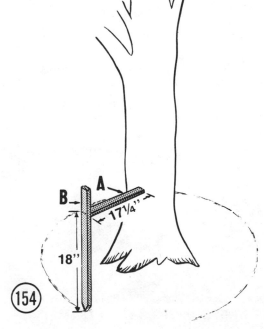

To estimate overall size of seat, notch A at end and 14" from end, Illus. 155. Drive a nail in position indicated. Place pencil in end notch and draw a circle on plywood. Place pencil in side notch to draw 14" width of seat.

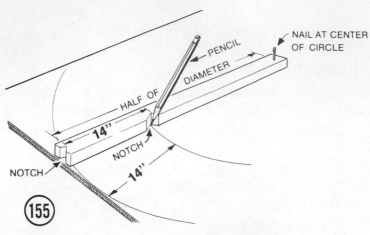

FOR TREES UP TO 30" IN DIAMETER

FOR TREES UP TO 12" IN DIAMETER

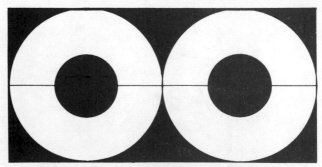

Cut four half circles from exterior grade plywood, Illus. 156. Place one in position so you can gauge position of four equally spaced posts, Illus. 157.

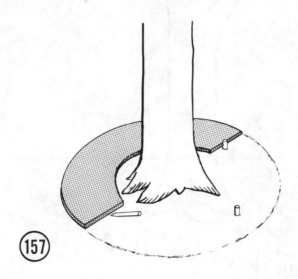

(157)

You can sharpen 4 x 4" posts at one end and drive them into ground, or dig holes at least 16 to 24" deep in position forms require. Posts must be plumb and level at 14" height. To insure being level and at equal height, set up guide lines. Check line with line level. Cut 6" forms to exact length required. Check to make certain each is plumb and level. Backfill to hold form in place. Drive two ½ or ⅝" reinforcing rods into area of form, Illus. 158.

Fill form with a wet mixture of one part cement, two parts sand to three parts gravel, or use a premix. Pour concrete to within 6" from top. Puddle concrete to eliminate any air holes. Use a sharpened 1 x 2.

Drill a ½" hole through 8" piece of ¼" plywood or through center of a paint stirrer. Place bolt in center of form. Screw nut on bolt so 1¼" of thread projects above stirrer. Complete filling form. Remove stirrer. Bolt should project 1½" above form, Illus. 159.

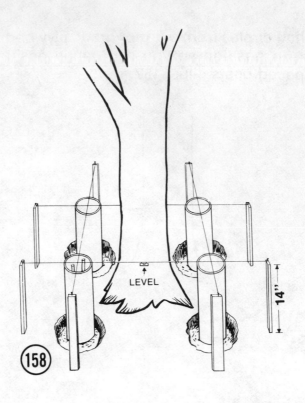

LEVEL

14"

(158)

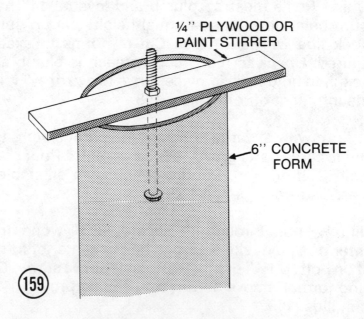

¼" PLYWOOD OR
PAINT STIRRER

6" CONCRETE
FORM

(159)

Drill 1" hole ½" deep in center of 2 x 4 x 12", Illus. 160. Then drill ½" hole through 2 x 4. Paint with wood preservative. When dry, apply one or two coats of exterior paint.

Drill four equally spaced ¼" holes through 2 x 4 x 12", Illus. 160. Pour form and compact concrete. Allow to set three days. Strip form.

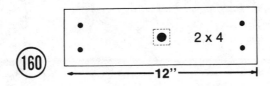

Fasten 2 x 4 to each post, Illus. 161.

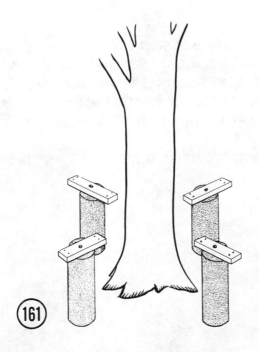

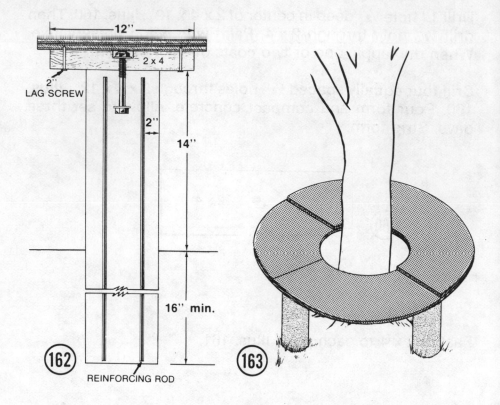

Fasten a single thickness of seat to 2 x 4. Drive 2" lag screws through 2 x 4 into seat, Illus. 162. Drill holes through lower section. Apply glue and clamp second section, Illus. 163, in position. Be sure to stagger joints. Fasten lower section to upper with 1¼" lag screws 1" from where joints overlap.

NOTE: If 4 x 4 posts are used, fasten 2 x 4 seat brace to post with ⅜ x 4" lag screw.

REPAIRING WATER LINE
BURIED IN A CONCRETE SLAB

In the late forties and through the fifties, many builders installed baseboard hot water heating, as well as slab radiation under concrete floors, Illus. 164. From an engineering standpoint, both systems looked like great ideas.

2 x 3 or 2 x 4 SLEEPER

REINFORCING WIRE

(164)

The concept, copper tubing buried in concrete and thus protected from damage, was sound since the waste heat would warm the concrete. But few installers reckoned with time and repair.

Slab radiation, where all tubing was embedded in concrete, depended entirely on warming the entire slab. What looked great on the designer's drawing board turned real sour as installation after installation went bad. One improperly soldered connection, a nail, cinder, or other foreign matter, buried alongside, could cause a leak few could find without chopping up a lot of concrete. As most slabs were laid over compacted soil, gravel or sand fill, the water leaked down, filled pockets before spreading sideways and up.

The first indication of a leak surfaces when water pressure continues to drop, Illus. 165. A pressure gauge will frequently drop even though an automatic valve, Illus. 166, feeds water to the system. Since most hot water heating systems are connected to a supply line with a pressure valve, water automatically flows when the system requires same. If the supply is shut down for repair, the heating unit could drain itself, and the pressure gauge would drop accordingly.

In a hilly neighborhood, houses on the highest points could, in times of low water pressure, be subjected to a syphoning action. Water under pressure that should flow into the system through a pressure valve designed to work only in one way, would allow water to be withdrawn if the valve became inoperative because of foreign matter.

110

Finding a leak buried in concrete normally requires taking up carpeting,* finished flooring or underlayment, then breaking into the concrete slab. Unless the homeowner knows where each line is buried, and has an accurate plan of the installation, he can be robbed blind. Locating a line, then a leak is quite a feat. It takes patience and a willingness to proceed very slowly. Unless great caution is taken, you can drive a chisel into copper tubing and cut copper even before you locate where it's buried.

When a pipe in a slab springs a leak, first try to contact the contractor who made the installation. If this isn't possible, ask your doctor if you can borrow a stethoscope. Request a demonstration so you will know how to use it. Then probe the floor. When you hear gurgling, you begin to zero in on the leaky spot. Using a carbide bit, carefully drill a test hole. Only drill a little at a time. Remove all dust to make certain you are still drilling in concrete and not copper.

As many floor slabs contain 2 x 3 or 2 x 4 sleepers A, Illus. 164, and wire reinforcing B, you will need to rent an electric hammer, a hand saw and wire cutters.

*Read Book #683 Carpeting Simplified.

Use extreme care when using an electric hammer. Wear safety goggles and only use the hammer after the dealer checks you out. An electric hammer is an easy tool for an intelligent, alert person to use, but a dangerous tool for anyone who doesn't recognize its power.

Always start a hole some distance away from where you think the pipe is located. Check your heating system to make certain a feeder line isn't located in area selected. A feeder line is one that supplies each radiator.

Advice from the contractor who made the installation can save considerable time and labor. Proceed cautiously as you break open a hole in concrete. Clear away loose particles. Wear goggles and chip away until you can get down to the gravel bed, then carefully enlarge hole until you can get a hand into the gravel. Remove gravel and earth until you begin to feel the wet spot, and the warmth of the pipe. It's a slow job. Once you have located the pipe, use a hammer and chisel, not an electric hammer.

When you find the leak, continue to open up slab so a plumber can sweat two nipples and a length of tubing. Or do it yourself following directions outlined in Books #675 and #682. If you have to saw through a length of sleeper, it's OK and it won't have to be replaced.

Once you have located the pipe, make a chart showing distance from wall, its direction and depth below floor. Also indicate position of feeder lines.

Leave repaired pipe exposed until you run a two or three day test. When replacing sand, make certain it doesn't contain any foreign matter, nails, cinders, etc. Screen it carefully and cover pipe. Repatch concrete. Replace underlayment, etc., and say a prayer of thanks that you could find and follow directions.

ADVICE TO THOSE PLANNING TO BUILD

If you lay a concrete slab over a hot water heating pipe or water line, don't cover pipe with concrete, Illus. 164. Build a form to keep concrete at least 4" from each pipe. Carefully screen sand to make certain it doesn't contain any nails, cinders, or other foreign matter. Fill area around pipe with sand. Draw a chart showing exact location of pipe. If at some future date, repairs are needed, you will not only know where to find the pipe, but will also cut repair costs to a minimum.

If you want to carpet over a concrete floor in a basement recreation room, or prefer laying a wood floor over the slab, embed pressure treated 2 x 4 sleepers every 16", Illus. 43. If pressure treated lumber isn't readily available, apply wood preservative before placing in position.

Drive 8 penny nails into sides to lock sleepers in place.

PAVEMENT REPAIRS

Remove all loose and broken pieces. Using a chisel, undercut as shown, Illus. 167. Hose edge of existing concrete and paint with a wet mix of cement and water. While still wet, fill area with concrete existing of one part cement, four parts of sand. For large areas, use a form to rebuild an edge, Illus. 168. Fill with 1:2¼:3 mix.

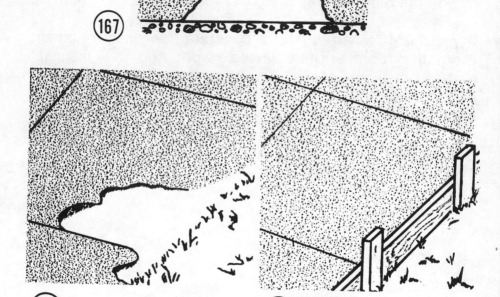

Since a cement and sand mix has a tendency to shrink, do this. Use a screed, Illus. 169, with a couple of nail heads in bottom edge. This permits leveling concrete with a slight rise. When concrete cures, it should finish level with existing slab.

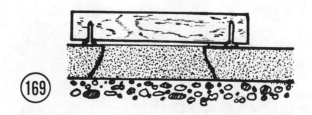

114

HOW TO BUILD A WATER STORAGE CISTERN

If you live in an area where water is in short supply, a build it yourself cistern, Illus. 170, can provide a reserve that might carry a garden through a bad drought. It can be especially helpful in case of fire.

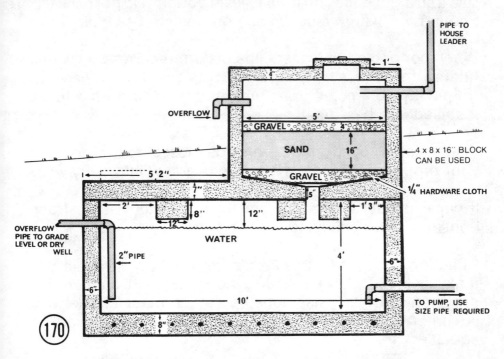

Locate cistern in a low area, some distance from your house. If your house is on a hillside, locate cistern where excavated earth can be banked around exposed side. While a cistern is a water-tight tank, the overflow could present a problem unless directed away from house.

A cistern can be built to any size or shape space permits. Leaders from gutters should be piped into cistern.

A filtering system of sand and gravel helps catch sediment. While it filters a lot of dirt, it still doesn't permit water to be used for cooking or drinking.

If you are building a new house, arrange to have excavating equipment dig a hole 2' larger in length and width than size of cistern. Top of cistern can be buried or exposed. Save all top soil. Pile it some distance from the excavation so it doesn't get mixed with subsoil. Use a pick and shovel to level bottom. Use a straight edge and level to level bottom. Do not back fill. Footing for cistern must be laid on undisturbed soil.

When connected to leaders, the cistern receives rain water filtered through stone, sand and gravel. Cistern water is frequently connected to a pump and used to flush a toilet installed in a basement.

Install cistern overflow pipe on side closest to low point of your property. If necessary, empty overflow into a dry well.

If water is vital for fire fighting, locate cistern as far from house or other buildings as your property permits.

Build form, Illus. 171. Use 2 x 8's for a 3000 gallon or larger tank, 2 x 6's for a 1000 to 2500 gallon tank. Paint lumber with old crankcase oil, nail together at corners, check with square. A form is considered square when diagonals are of equal length.

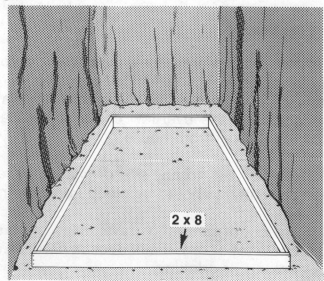

2 x 8

171

Wire ½" reinforcing rods together, 12" on centers, to reinforce floor slab. If you plan on pouring foundation walls, embed ½" reinforcing rods by length required, 12" on centers, Illus. 19,172. Position these vertically around perimeter, 3" in from outside edge. Do not embed rods vertically if you build sides with concrete blocks.

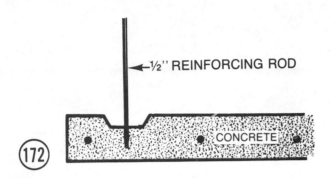

Position a form for overflow pipe, pipe for pump, another for leader pipe, in position prior to pouring walls, Illus. 61.

If you install a cistern in an area where rock prevents digging to depth desired, use excavated soil to bank around finished cistern.

Allow 12" air space between water and top of cistern, Illus. 170. In locating cistern, keep water level below frost level.

After leveling excavation and checking same with a straight edge and level, build forms to size required. These can be nailed at corners with 8 penny nails. Check with square; double check by measuring diagonals. Cut ½" reinforcing rods length required. Lay in position, Illus. 173, 1' on centers. Wire rods together. Raise reinforcing about 1 or 2" above ground by inserting stone or globs of concrete. Pour concrete floor in one pouring. Use one part cement to three parts sand to five parts gravel. To pour a watertight joint, drill 1" holes, one foot on centers, through 2 x 4's, Illus. 174.

117

Bevel to 45°, then saw in half, Illus. 175. When you have poured slab to within 1½" from top, position 2 x 4, Illus. 174, flush with top edge of form. These form a key to receive poured walls.

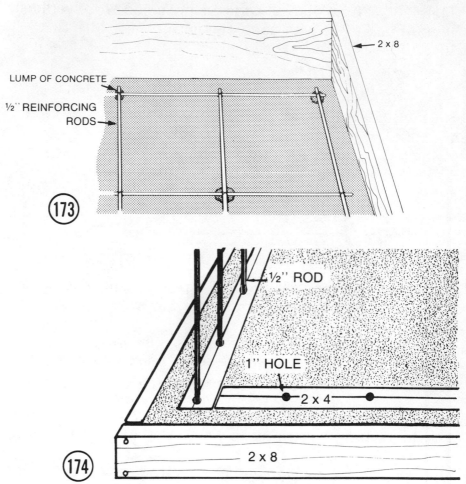

2 x 8

LUMP OF CONCRETE

½" REINFORCING RODS

(173)

½" ROD

1" HOLE

2 x 4

2 x 8

(174)

Cut key in half
to simplify removal.

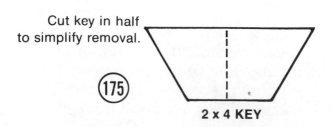

(175)

2 x 4 KEY

Embed vertical rods 12" on centers, Illus. 172. As soon as a slab begins to set, carefully remove 2 x 4's. Allow floor to set at least three days before building forms for walls. Paint inside face of ½" plywood with old crankcase oil. Cut ½" reinforcing rods to length required to run horizontally, wire in position, Illus. 19. Cut ½" plywood for inner form. Drill holes through forms and fasten together with cross ties.

Whether you lay up block, or build forms and pour foundation, allow for a recess in top course for the three 8 x 12" joists, in position indicated, Illus. 170, 176. These provide support for filtering bed.

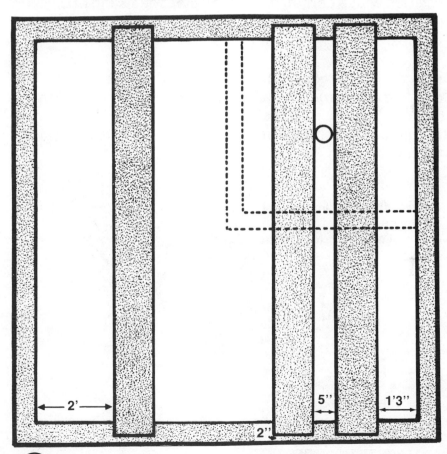

176

To allow water to enter filtering bed, use a piece of 6" drain tile cut to 5" length. Slope floor of filtering bed to shape shown. Lock drain tile in position flush with floor. Pour sides of sand storage bed or use 4 x 8 x 16" concrete block.

Lay ¼" hardware cloth over sloped floor. Cover with 3 to 4" of ¾" gravel, a 16" bed of sand, plus 4" of ¾" gravel.

Use readymix concrete if available so you can pour entire form in one pouring. Use a broom handle or similar type stick to work concrete down around reinforcing. Allow walls to set at least three days before stripping forms. Plaster inside face of cistern with a parging coat of plaster consisting of one part cement to two parts of finely screened sand. Calk pipe joints with cement after removing forms.

Build or buy precast joists and slabs for top, Illus. 177. Schedule delivery of each so truck can place them in position. Embed an 8" length of 4" drain tile in top of one slab, Illus. 178. This permits venting cistern. A cap can be added if desired.

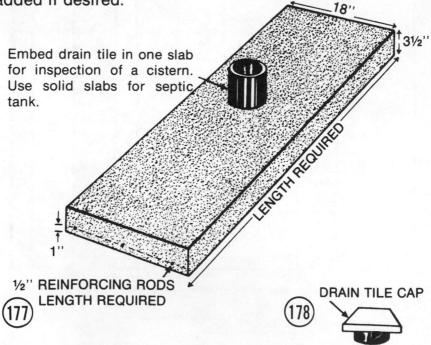

Embed drain tile in one slab for inspection of a cistern. Use solid slabs for septic tank.

18"

3½"

LENGTH REQUIRED

1"

½" REINFORCING RODS LENGTH REQUIRED

(177)

DRAIN TILE CAP

(178)

To cast cistern cover slabs, use 2 x 4 form, Illus. 179.

If filter bed is below grade, extend vent pipe in slab cover to above grade.

Install pump size desired.

To pour a single slab, Illus. 179, use ⅝ or ¾ x 3 x 8' plywood for A. This must be painted with oil before use and hosed out after each pouring. Place A on three 2 x 4 B. Check with level. Use 2 x 4 x 2' for C, 2 x 4 by length required for E. Use 1 x 4 for DFG. Cut D 12" for a 12" wide slab, 18" for a larger one. While both a 12 and 18" wide slab require two strong men to move, build to width tank requires. Embed three ⅜" reinforcing rods in each slab, 1" from bottom face, Illus. 177.

Oil D and E with crankcase oil prior to each use. Position D, then E. Nail F to A. Drive G in place. Wire two ⅜" reinforcing rod handles, Illus. 180, in position. Pour slab using a mix consisting of one part cement, 2¼ parts sand, 3 parts ¾" gravel.

Four slabs can be poured at one time as shown, Illus. 181.

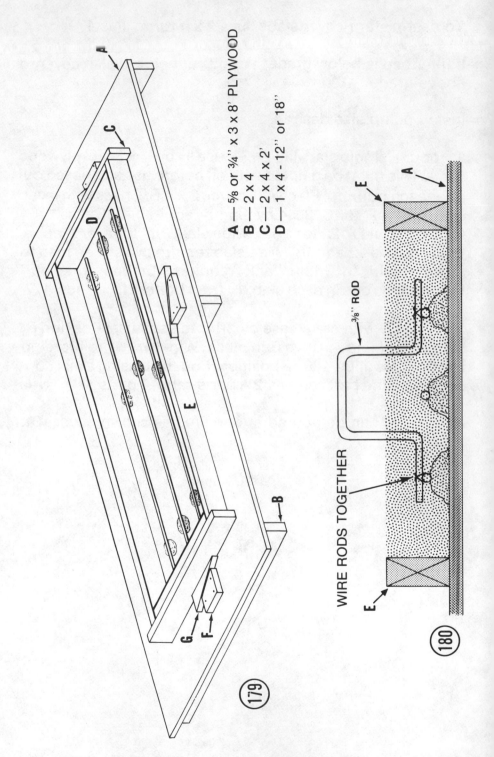

A — ⅝ or ¾" x 3 x 8' PLYWOOD
B — 2 x 4
C — 2 x 4 x 2'
D — 1 x 4 - 12" or 18"

179

⅜" ROD

WIRE RODS TOGETHER

E

A

E

180

122

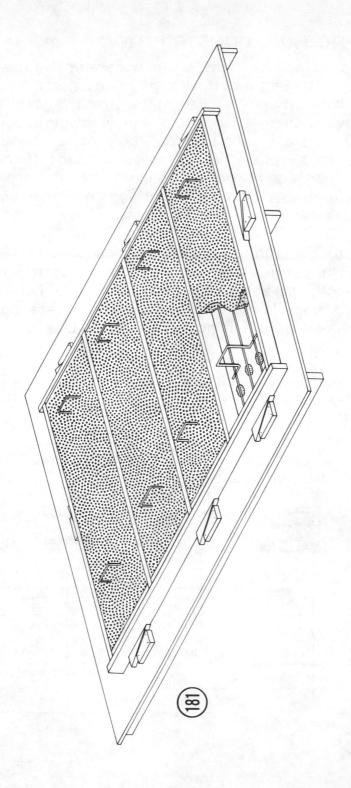

SEPTIC TANK CONSTRUCTION

Before buying property in an undeveloped area, inquire whether the Board of Health will issue a permit for a septic tank. If the property is adjacent to a stream or lake that's part of a watershed, or close to a well supplying a community water system, a permit will only be granted if the tank and field can be placed an approved distance. If the parcel doesn't provide the needed space, no permit will be issued. In many areas, a building permit won't be issued unless you obtain a septic tank permit.

Before signing any purchase agreement, ascertain whether a septic tank permit was previously refused. Smart purchasers frequently save themselves considerable heartache by having their lawyer make a land purchase agreement contingent on obtaining both a septic tank and building permit.

Also consider whether the location selected for a tank and field allows sufficient clear space for a house, garage and driveway.

Illus. 182 indicates the various size tanks required for 2, 3, 4 and 5 bedroom houses.

Recommended Septic Tank Capacities

| No. of bedrooms in dwelling | Capacity per bedroom in gallons | Required total tank capacity in gallons | Tank Size | | | |
			Inside width	Inside length	Liquid depth	Total depth
2 or less	375	750	3 ft. 6 in.	7 ft. 6 in.	4 ft. 0 in.	5 ft. 0 in.
3	300	900	3 ft. 6 in.	8 ft. 0 in.	4 ft. 6 in.	5 ft. 6 in.
4	250	1,000	4 ft. 0 in.	8 ft. 0 in.	4 ft. 6 in.	5 ft. 6 in.
5	250	1,250	4 ft. 0 in.	9 ft. 0 in.	4 ft. 6 in.	5 ft. 6 in.

(182)

Prospective land buyers who plan on building outside a sewer district should study the installation of a septic tank and field. Most communities adjacent to any city only grant a permit if the tank is placed 5' or more from the house, at least 50' from a cistern, 100' from a well, and the field is not closer than 10' from property line, Illus. 183.

When selecting a site, be sure to consider wells, cisterns or streams on your neighbor's property.

As noted in Illus. 183, 184, codes specify hub and spigot, or hubless cast iron sewer pipe between house and septic tank. This must be 5'0'' or longer. Cast iron or bituminous sewer pipe is acceptable between the septic tank and either a junction or distribution box.

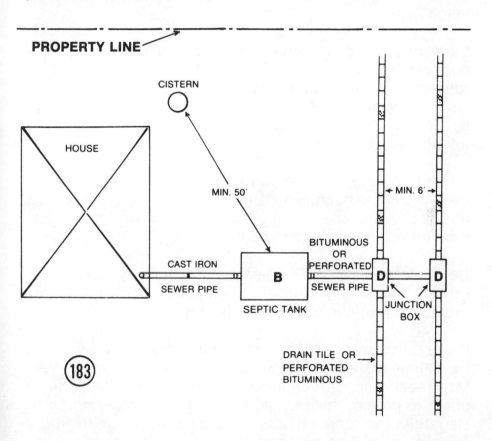

The sewer line between house and septic tank must slope at least ¼" to 1" per foot, as must the line between the tank and junction box. Follow local code requirements. The septic tank must be level.

The area required for the field is determined by the number of lineal feet the field requires. You can run this in two, three or as many rows as shape of space permits. Most codes specify a 6' minimum spacing between fields.

A septic tank and field should never be located in a low, wet area, or on rock. Select an open area where trees or shrubs will not send roots down to the tile. After selecting a site, call the Department of Health. Inquire whether they wish to make a free inspection. They will advise what must be done to pass inspection.

Most inspectors not only inspect the site, make inquiry concerning the number of bedrooms the house will contain, recommend size of tank, shape and length of field, but will also make an absorption test to ascertain how fast the subsoil will absorb water. Or they will advise you how to make a test.

While installing a system is relatively simple, a septic tank installation can become real sticky when you learn that such and such a septic tank company can obtain a permit for you, then quotes an exorbitant cost.

Regardless of what an "in" septic tank company may tell you, no one can stop you from making your own installation, providing you follow local regulations.

If you think anyone in the health department is giving you a hard time, there are two good reasons why this may be so. Most health departments make an honest and determined effort to protect the area adjacent to water shed property. Regardless of whether it's a nearby stream, runoff into a stream, or a well on your property or neighbor's property, the field must be laid according to regulation. The second reason is financial. If a local septic company has a monopoly, they may overcharge.

If you read and learn how to install a septic tank before you start talking business to an installer, you will save yourself a lot of time, money and aggravation. If you then decide to do part or all the work, you can save even more money. Either way, you get a better job when you know what needs to be done.

A septic tank system consists of a large metal or concrete holding tank B, Illus. 184; a distribution center D; and a field of 4'' diameter perforated drain tile C. Many codes permit installation without a distribution box. They allow junction boxes as shown in Illus. 183.

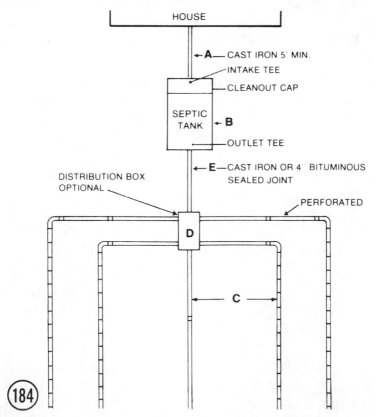

The sewer line E, Illus. 184, must be 4" hub and spigot or hubless cast iron, 5'0" or more in length. Hubless 4" cast iron, now available in many areas, is also approved by most health departments.

It's best to buy a precast or metal septic tank. These are now readily available. If you decide to build, use 2 x 6 for footing forms. Use blocks or erect forms and pour tank in place. Reinforce sides and bottom with ½" rods, or use 6 x 6" reinforcing wire.

Since tanks purchased readymade will be delivered by a truck with a crane that positions the tank level in the excavation you have prepared, the question you must resolve is whether the site selected for the tank can be reached by a truck. Give consideration to this simple but important fact since once you start excavating for a house you might not be able to truck and crane a tank into position.

If you prefer to pour a tank in place, will a readymix truck be able to come close enough to chute or wheelbarrow the readymix? Or does the location of the site automatically require you rent a concrete mixing machine and do the work on the site? With planks properly placed to form a level, or downhill walk, two or three willing souls can usually wheelbarrow concrete from a ready mix truck fast enough to pour a tank without paying overtime for a waiting truck. If you decide to buy readymix, ask the company how long you can hold the truck on the job before overtime sets in.

Always check tank with a level to make certain it's both plumb and level after it's placed in position, and before truck leaves.

Trenches for a field are usually 18" wide and to a depth that permits 4 to 6" of gravel on bottom, 4" tile, plus 2 to 4" of gravel on top, Illus. 185. Cover gravel with strips of #15 felt before backfilling trench. The 4" drain tile used in the field

128

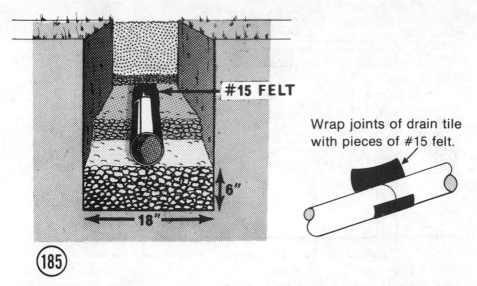

#15 FELT

Wrap joints of drain tile with pieces of #15 felt.

6"

18"

(185)

must be placed at a pitch codes specify. This could be 2 to 4" in 100'.

If you buy a precast or metal tank, buy the size your family requires, or one size larger. Buy a size that would be required if you add extra bedroms at some future date. There is no economy in putting in a minimum approved size when a larger size only costs a few dollars more.

If you buy a complete installation, the installer will excavate for the tank and trench the field. If you dig, be sure to excavate to exact depth Health Department suggests. Make certain bottom is level. Use a straight 2 x 4 and a level to check bottom of excavation. The depth and size of hole for a tank is determined by its size and shape.

Since the sewer line from the house to the tank must pitch ¼" per foot, or pitch local codes require, the depth of the hole will be determined by the intake TEE, Illus. 186. Dig trench from house to selected site. Slope gravel bed to pitch pipe requires. When 5'0" or further away, place a TEE, Illus. 187, in position on the end of the pipe. To estimate depth of excavation, measure from bottom of TEE to depth below TEE your tank requires. Note position of inlet TEE, Illus. 186.

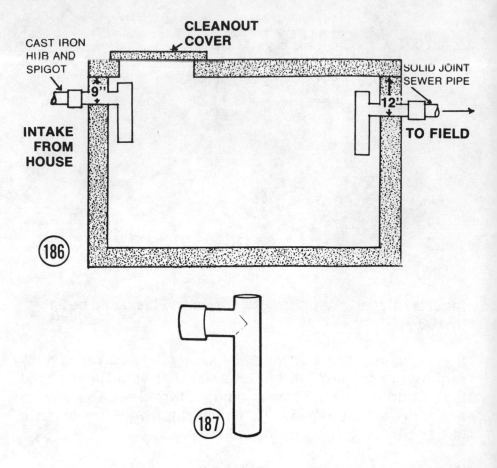

Codes recommend outlet TEE be placed 3" lower than inlet.

When installing a new tank, always install a cleanout plug, Illus. 188, in direct line with the inlet TEE. This greatly simplifies servicing a septic tank.

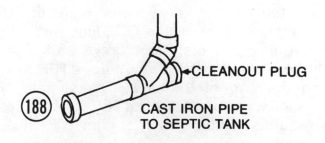

When installing a septic field on rolling or hilly land, level the area required.

A septic tank can also be built with concrete blocks. Excavate to size and depth tank requires. Level bottom, then dig a 10" wide footing trench, 4" lower than floor, around perimeter of floor area. Lay a thick bed of mortar and position a starter course of 10 x 8 x 16 or 18" blocks. These will project 4" above the floor area.

Cut 6 x 6" reinforcing wire to size floor area requires. Raise wire about 1" and pour floor flush with top of block. Fill core of block with concrete. Allow slab to set three days, then build walls using 8 x 8 x 16 or 18" blocks. These are placed flush with inside edge of 10" block. Fill cores of the first three courses with concrete. If you are building a large tank, lay reinforcing wire, Illus. 66, in every third course of block.

Set Inlet Tee and Outlet Tee in position shown, Illus. 186.

Finish inside face as shown, Illus. 50,51,52,53. Allow tank to set at least five days, then paint inside and outside with hot tar or asphalt cement.

Follow local code requirements, and lay tile to depth specified. Cover with gravel specified, then cover gravel with #15 felt before backfilling. Since the Board of Health will want to make an inspection before you cover the field, follow directions they provide, and under no circumstances give the inspector a hard time.

When laying perforated bituminous field tile, follow local code recommendations regarding a distribution box, Illus. 184, or junction boxes, Illus. 183.

CONCRETE FENCE POSTS

(189)

Homeowners who have had it with their neighbors, children or dogs, discover wire fencing can be a great pain reliever. While Book #607 How to Build Fences, Gates, Outdoor Projects, explains how to build handsome wood fencing, a quick and economical solution can be achieved with wire fencing and concrete posts. Since wood posts frequently rot in a relatively short span of time, a reinforced concrete post set in a bed of concrete, Illus. 190, encourages instant peace of mind that can last a long time. Sinking a 7'0" post 30" below grade, and filling hole with concrete, provides a rot proof fence post.

Select wire fencing you want to install. You can pour one or up to seven posts at one time using the form shown, Illus. 191. Build form as explained on page 121. This form permits pouring 3½ x 3½ x 7'0" posts.

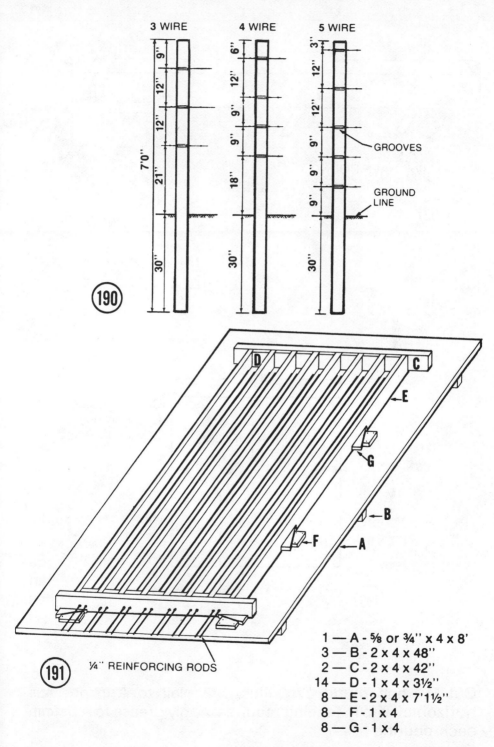

3 WIRE

9"
12"
12"
7'0"
21"
30"

4 WIRE

6"
12"
9"
9"
18"
30"

5 WIRE

3"
12"
12"
9"
9"
9"
GROOVES
9"
GROUND
LINE
30"

⑲⓪

⑲①   ¼" REINFORCING RODS

1 — A - ⅝ or ¾" x 4 x 8'
3 — B - 2 x 4 x 48"
2 — C - 2 x 4 x 42"
14 — D - 1 x 4 x 3½"
8 — E - 2 x 4 x 7'1½"
8 — F - 1 x 4
8 — G - 1 x 4

133

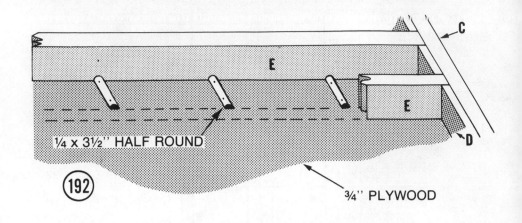

¼ x 3½" HALF ROUND

(192)

¾" PLYWOOD

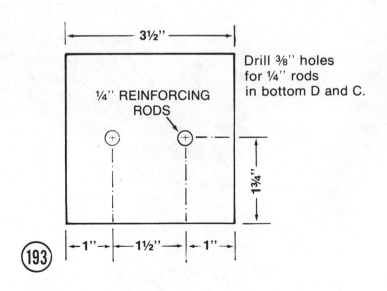

3½"

¼" REINFORCING RODS

Drill ⅜" holes for ¼" rods in bottom D and C.

1¾"

←1"→ ←1½"→ ←1"→

(193)

Cut ¼" half round 3½", Illus. 192. Nail to A in position horizontal wire in fencing requires. Apply grease to A before each pouring.

134

To anchor each post to concrete poured in post hole, cut ¼ or ⅜" reinforcing rods 6" longer than form. Use two rods for each post. Drill holes in C and D in position shown, Illus. 193. Paint form with oil before pouring concrete. Hose out form after removing posts.

Position rods in form on globs of concrete approximately 1¾" from bottom of form and 3" from D at top. Place globs of concrete over ¼ x 3½" half round. Pack these globs over half round and it insures making a neat indent for wire. Use one bag of cement to 2¼ cubic feet of sand, plus 2½ cubic feet of ¾" maximum size gravel. Trowel surface after pouring. Allow to set 48 hours before removing from form.

Dig 8 or 10" diameter post holes, 30" or depth post requires. Dig all holes to a guide line. You can bend projecting end of rod to a slight angle to lock it securely in concrete, or leave it straight. Embed each post in concrete. Use 1 part cement, 2 parts sand, 3 parts small gravel. Set up a guide line to indicate overall height of post. Check each post with a level in two directions as you fill hole with concrete. Allow posts to set a week before wiring fencing to post.

NOTE: Don't use barbed wire. While some neighbors might deserve it, few local ordinances permit same.

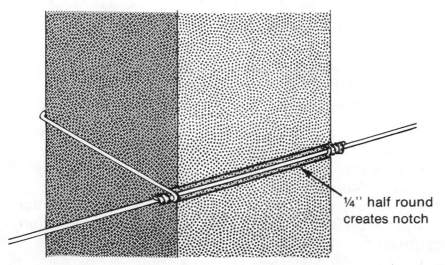

¼" half round creates notch

LIFETIME PICNIC TABLE

(194)

LIST OF MATERIAL

    2 — 6 or 8" x 5' concrete form A
    1 — 2 x 4 x 8' B,D
    1 — 2 x 6 x 10' C
    3 — 2 x 10 x 14' E,F
    2 — 1 x 2 x 10'
    8 — ½ x 7" carriage bolts, nuts, washers
    4 — ½ x 5"   "   "   "   "
   24 — 2¾" No. 14 flathead screws
    4 — ¼ x 44" reinforcing rod
        Wood preservative

Homeowners who know how quickly a wood post can rot away in some soil appreciate the "lifetime" quality of building a picnic table on concrete posts.

Six inch diameter concrete forms, Illus. 195, available from most masonry supply retailers, simplify pouring posts.

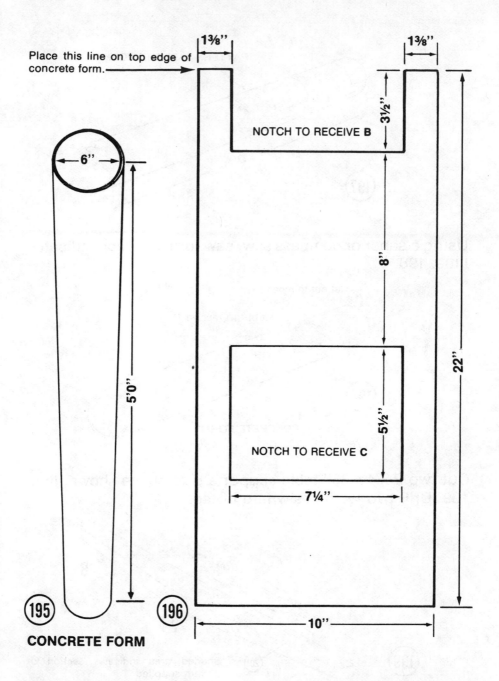

Place this line on top edge of concrete form.

1⅜"

1⅜"

3½"

NOTCH TO RECEIVE **B**

8"

22"

6"

5'0"

5½"

NOTCH TO RECEIVE **C**

7¼"

(195)

CONCRETE FORM

(196)

10"

To cut form to exact shape required, draw a full size pattern using dimensions shown, Illus. 196. Tape pattern to form, Illus. 197. Using a marking pen, draw outline on 6" x 5' form,

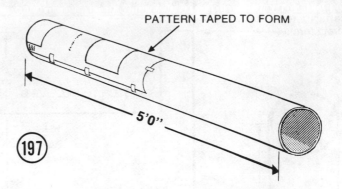

PATTERN TAPED TO FORM

5'0"

(197)

Using a saber or compass saw, saw form to shape indicated, Illus. 198.

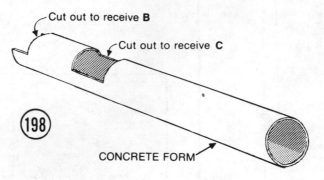

Cut out to receive **B**

Cut out to receive **C**

(198)

CONCRETE FORM

Cut two 2 x 4 x 36'' table supports B to shape shown, Illus. 199. Drill two ½'' holes where noted.

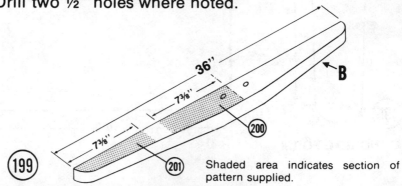

36"

B

7³⁄₈"

(200)

7³⁄₈"

(199)

(201)

Shaded area indicates section of pattern supplied.

Illus. 200 and 201 are full size patterns for curved parts of B. Draw up a full size pattern for one half of B and trace same on a 2 x 4 x 36''.

138

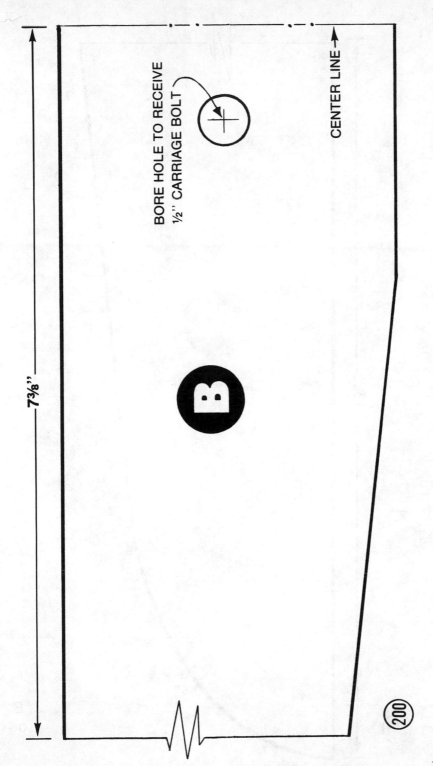

BORE HOLE TO RECEIVE
½" CARRIAGE BOLT

CENTER LINE →

7⅜"

B

200

139

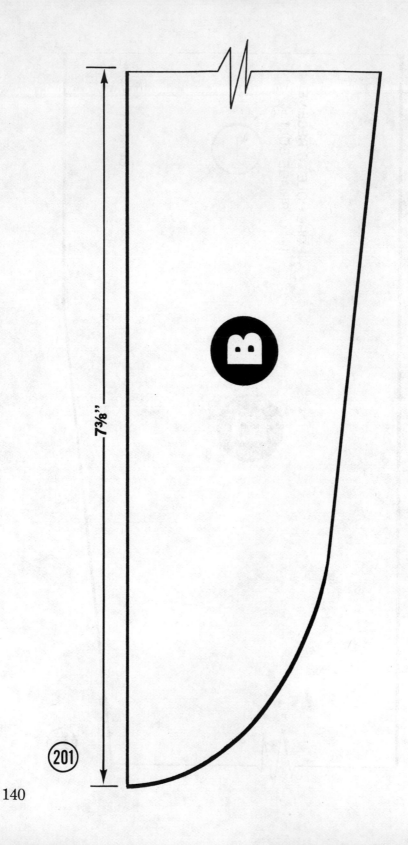

7⅜"

B

(201)

Center B in form, Illus. 202. Drill two ½" holes through form. Bolt B to form with two ½ x 7" carriage bolts. Finger tighten nuts. Don't distort shape of form.

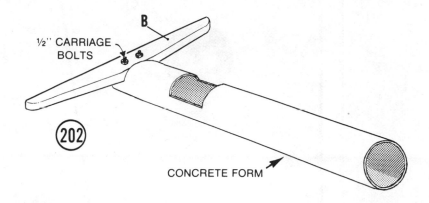

Cut two 2 x 6 x 5' C, Illus. 203, to shape shown. Drill ½" holes in position indicated. Fasten C to form with two bolts, Illus. 205.

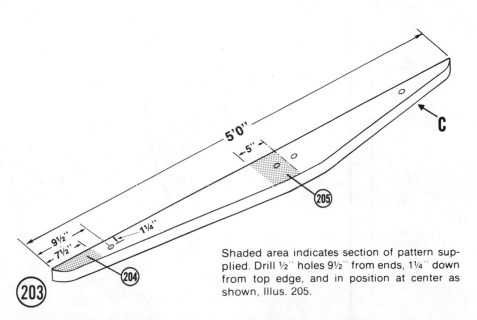

Shaded area indicates section of pattern supplied. Drill ½" holes 9½" from ends, 1¼" down from top edge, and in position at center as shown, Illus. 205.

Illus. 204 and 205 are full size patterns for curved part of C. Draw up a full size pattern for one half of C.

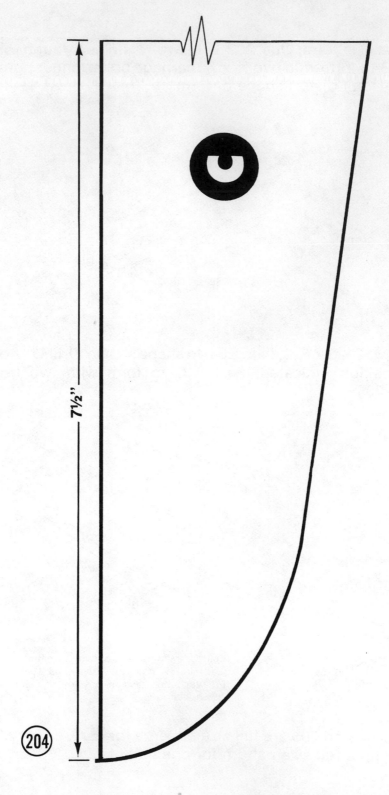

7½"

204

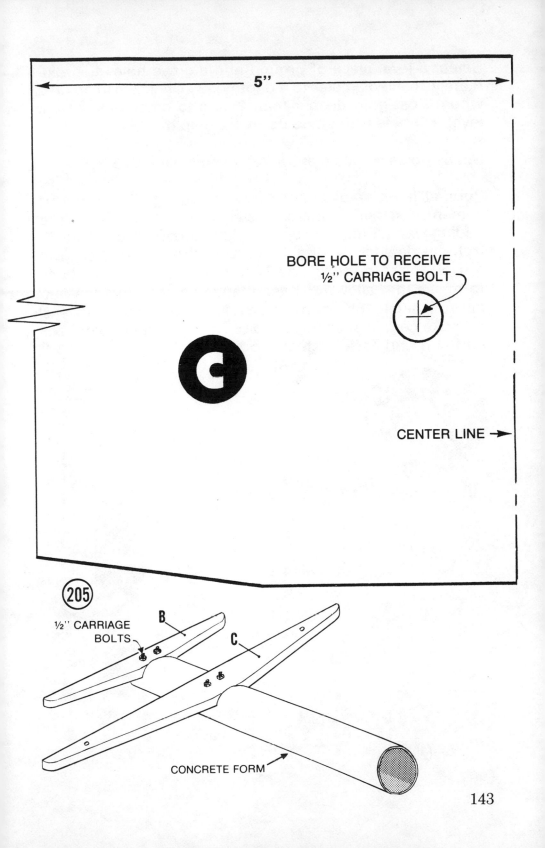

5"

BORE HOLE TO RECEIVE
½'' CARRIAGE BOLT

CENTER LINE →

(205)

½'' CARRIAGE
BOLTS

B

C

CONCRETE FORM

143

Select a level piece of ground and dig two holes approximately 16" in diameter to a depth of 2'. If you live in an area where frost goes deeper than 2', dig to depth below frost level. Fill hole with stone up to a 2' depth.

Space holes so posts allow 72" overall, Illus. 206,208.

Pour at least 4" of concrete for a footing. Use one part cement, two sand, three gravel. Mix thoroughly before adding water. Embed two ⅜" x 6' reinforcing rods about 1" from inside edge of form. Drive rods through concrete into gravel. Top of rod should be 2 or 3" below top of form. Check forms so they allow 72" overall and position top edge of C approximately 16½" above grade, Illus. 208. Check with level to make certain each form is plumb. Pour concrete or pack earth around base to steady form, Illus. 207.

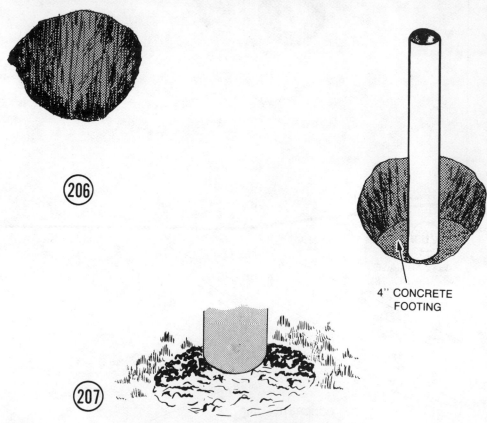

206

4" CONCRETE
FOOTING

207

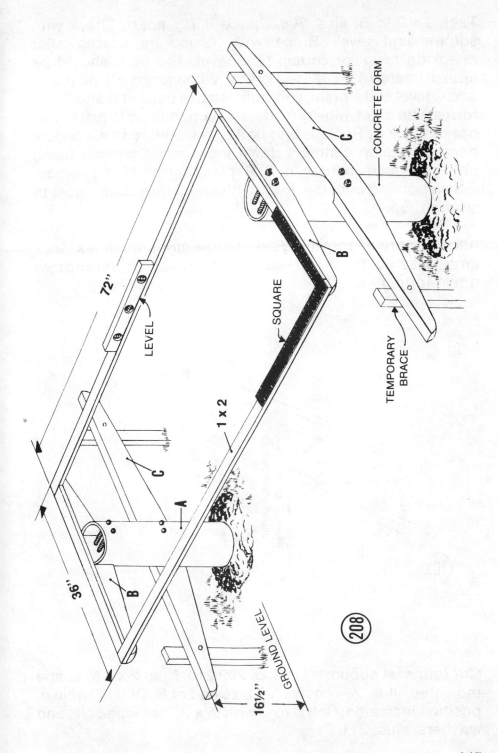

72"

36"

16½"

LEVEL

SQUARE

1 x 2

CONCRETE FORM

TEMPORARY BRACE

GROUND LEVEL

A

B

C

208

145

Tack 1 x 2 to B, Illus. 208. Space B 72" apart. Check with square and level. Brace with temporary braces after checking to make certain C is level. Top of C should be approximately 16½" above grade. When forms are plumb, B and C level and square, carefully remove bolts at B and C. Fill forms with a wet, mushy mixture of concrete up to just below opening for C. Replace and bolt C in position. Use a broom handle to tamp concrete down into form. Continue filling until you reach opening for B. Replace and bolt B in position. Finish pouring concrete flush with top of form. Use a float to smooth top.

Allow concrete to set three days before stripping forms. Set a circular saw blade to just less than thickness of form and saw down form, Illus. 209.

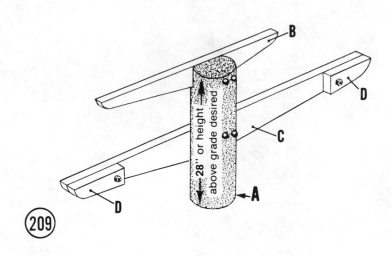

Cut four seat supports D, Illus. 209,210, from 2 x 4 to shape indicated. Illus. 204 shows full size end of D. Drill ½" hole in position indicated. Bolt D to C with ½ x 5" carriage bolts and washers, Illus. 211.

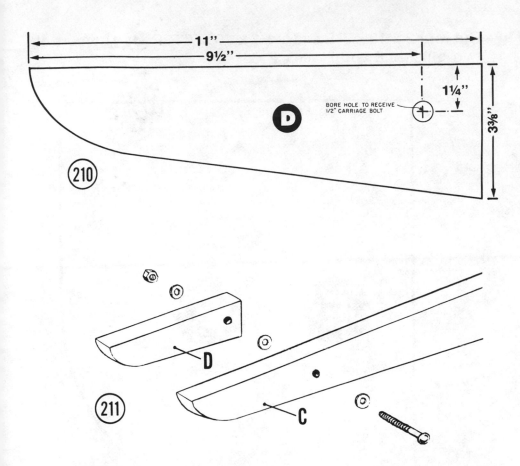

11"

9½"

BORE HOLE TO RECEIVE
1/2" CARRIAGE BOLT

D

1¼"

3⅜"

210

211

D

C

Bore shank and pilot holes, Illus. 212, to size screw requires.
Drill shank hole to size that permits free entry of screw. Drill
pilot hole slightly less than threaded portion of screw, and
only half its depth. Use a countersink bit to bevel edge of
shank hole to receive head of screw.

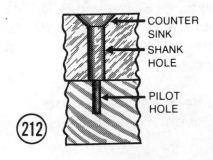

COUNTER
SINK

SHANK
HOLE

PILOT
HOLE

212

Cut four 2 x 10 x 7' E and two 2 x 10 x 7' F. Round corners of two outside E and F, Illus. 213.

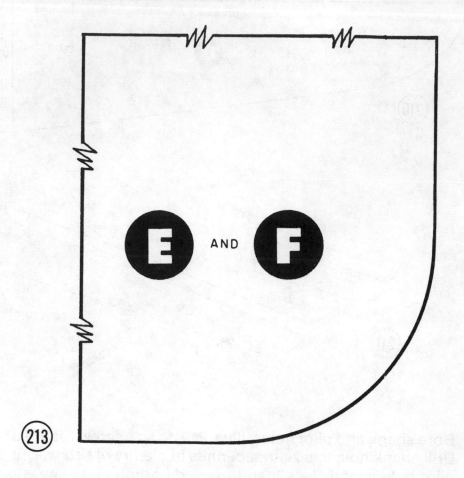

Place E on B. E extends 6" beyond B. Drill ¼" holes in E so E can be screwed to B. Use 2¾" No. 14 flathead screws. Allow ¼" spacings between E, Illus. 214. Countersink all screws, fill holes with a wood filler.

Test sit opening before screwing F to D. Follow procedure outlined for E. D permits raising seats vertically when not in use.

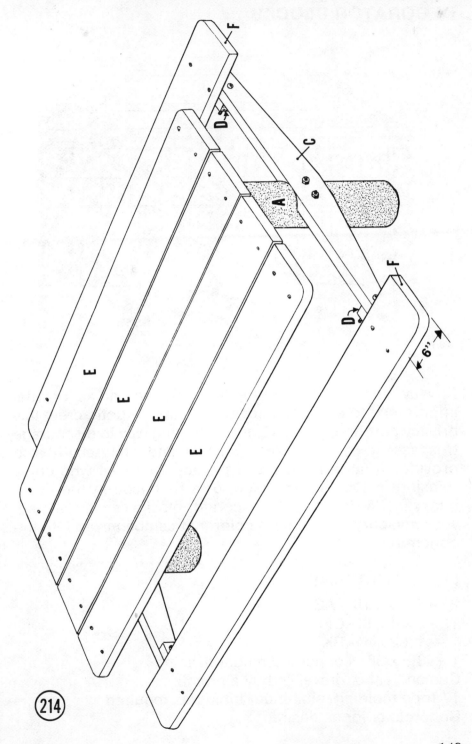

DECORATOR BLOCKS

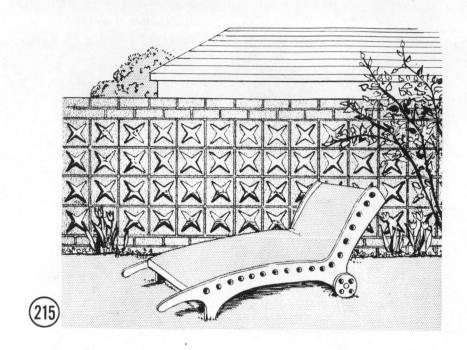

Privacy and property protection are two areas of vital importance to every homeowner. To insure both, erect this privacy partition, Illus. 215. It goes a long way to discourage trespassing by neighbors, animals and children. It also provides a large measure of privacy for those who enjoy relaxing in the sun or shade, or a barbecue in their own backyard. While concrete decorator blocks can be painted, your masonry retailer sells color that can be mixed into the concrete.

LIST OF MATERIAL
2 — 2 x 4 x 10' - AE
1 — 2 x 4 x 6' - CFH
1 — 1 x 2 x 4' - BK
1 — 3½ x 36'' copper aluminum flashing
Cement, sand, gravel or buy a premix
1'' rope molding, aluminum tubing as required
Concrete color as desired

150

While decorative blocks can be purchased readymade, considerable savings can be effected when you cast them. Several can be made for less than one costs readymade. Since these blocks have many end uses they prove popular sellers.

Originally designed for fencing, Illus. 216, the blocks can be laid three to four high.

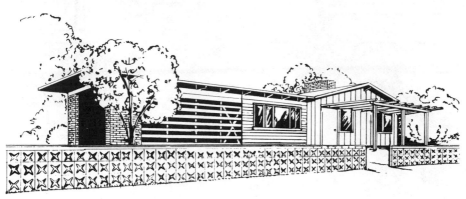

(216)

Indoor and outdoor planters, Illus. 217,218, and interior partitions, Illus. 219, are other popular areas.

(217)

(218)

(219)

As step by step directions suggest, building a form, Illus. 220, permits pouring five blocks at one time, Illus. 221.

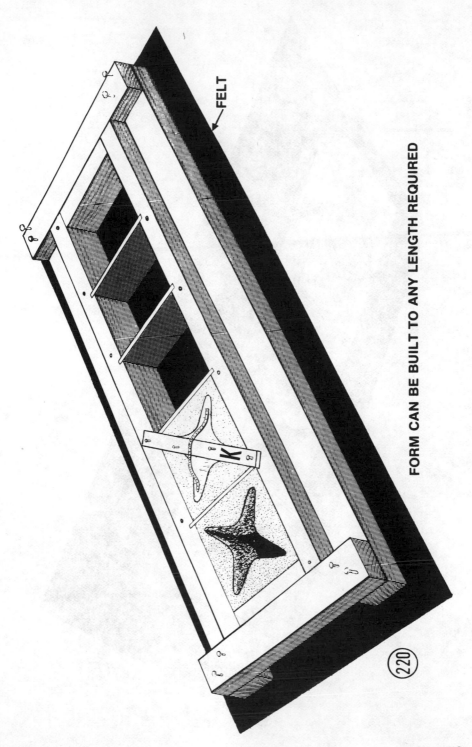

FELT

K

FORM CAN BE BUILT TO ANY LENGTH REQUIRED

(220)

153

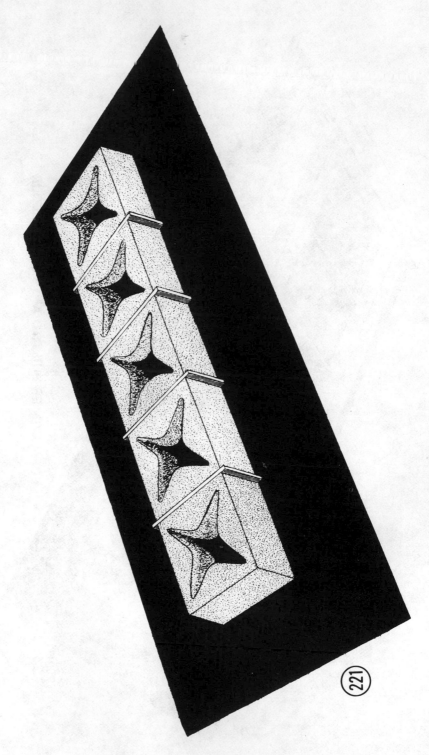

Cut two 2 x 4 x 56⅛" A, Illus. 222. Position on 2 x 4's. Select a level area. Nail 1 x 2 cleats B across A. Do not drive nails home. Saw, chisel and rout out ¼" wide, ¼" deep grooves in position indicated. Use a router with a ¼" bit set to rout ¼" deep, or clamp a piece of 2 x 4 alongside line and use it as a saw guide. Make two cuts, then use a ¼" chisel. Remove 1 x 2 B.

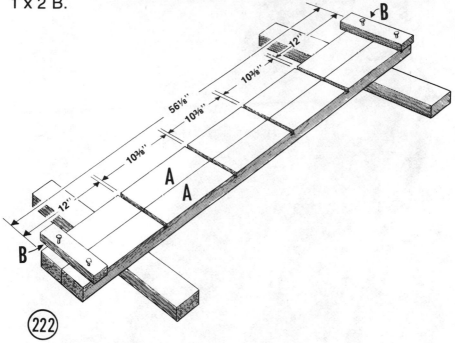

Cut two 2 x 4 x 10⅜" C, Illus. 223.

Cut four ¼ x 3½ x 10⅞" D, Illus. 224, from plywood. Apply old crankcase oil to D before each use.

Cut two 2 x 4 x 63⅜" E, two 2 x 4 x 20⅜" F, Illus. 225.

Select a perfectly level area. If same isn't readily available, level up a ¾" panel of plywood. Cover with polyethylene or #15 roofing felt. Place form in position, Illus. 225. Check with square and level. Drill two 3/16" holes through F, approximately 1" into E, at all four corners. Drop a 16 or 20 penny nail into each hole. Apply a little oil to nail so it can easily be removed.

155

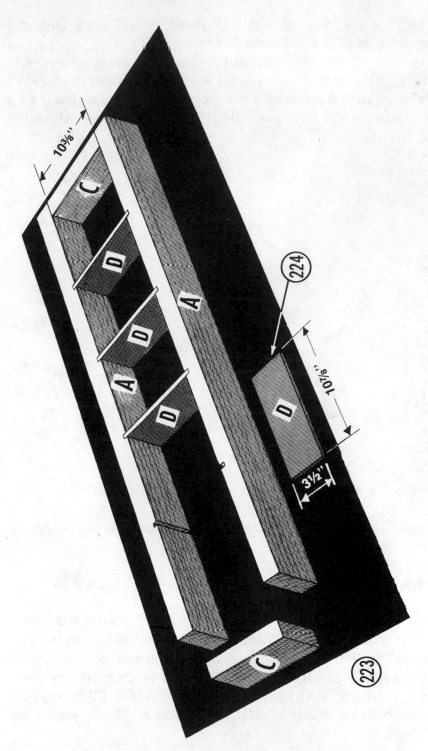

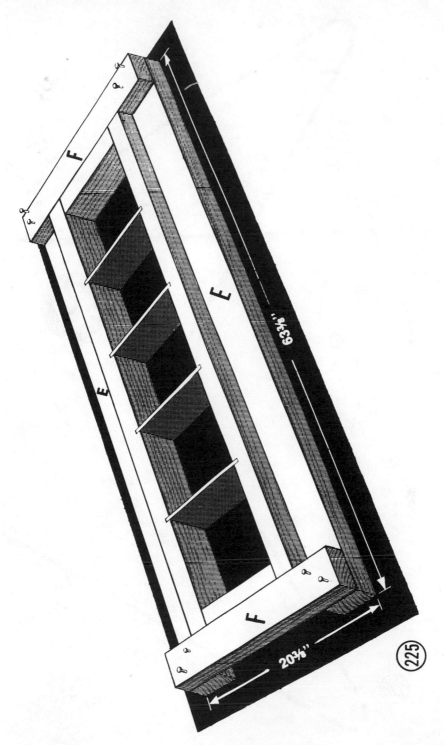

F

F

E

E

63¾"

20¾"

225

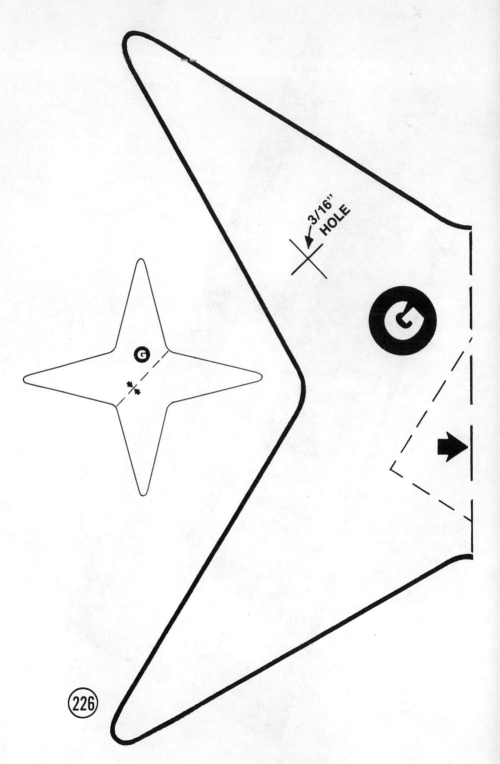

3/16" HOLE

G

226

158

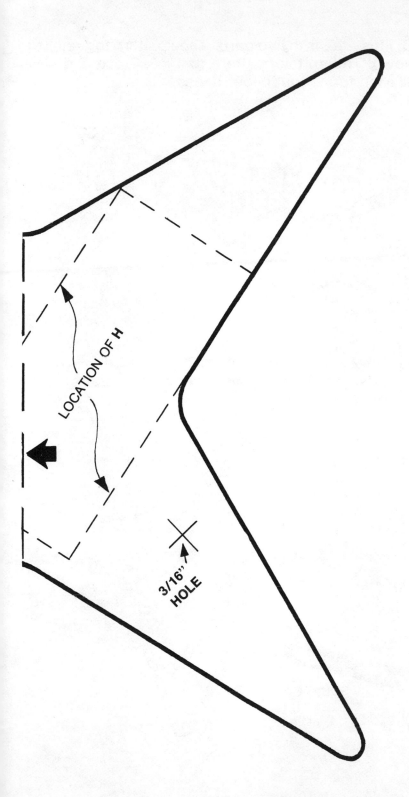

LOCATION OF **H**

3/16"
HOLE

159

Pattern G, Illus. 226, is in two parts. Tape pattern together to shape shown. Thumb tack pattern to 1 x 8. Trace and saw two G for each form. Sandpaper edges.

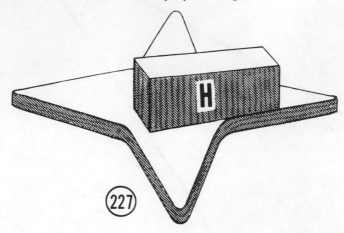

Cut a piece of 2 x 4 x 2'' for H, Illus. 227. Nail G to H with 4 penny nails. Using a square to make certain both parts are in position, Illus. 228, nail second G to H.

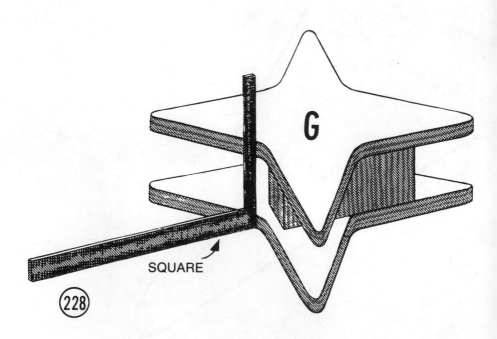

SQUARE

Cut a 3½ x 36" strip of copper or aluminum flashing. Nail flashing to form, Illus. 229, using ¾" brads. Cut flashing so ends butt together on H. Do not overlap.

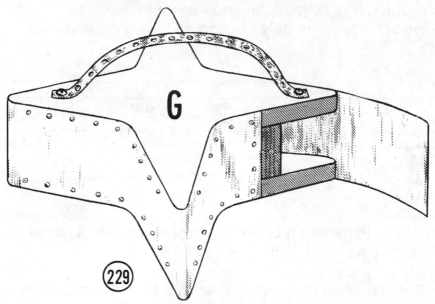

Screw a 12" length of plumbers strap or clothes line to G, Illus. 230.

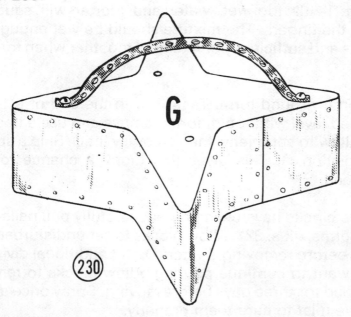

Cut one 1 x 2 x 20" K. Drill four 3/16" holes in position shown, Illus. 231. Place K in position diagonally across G, Illus. 220. Mark and drill two 3/16" holes in G. Place two nails through K into G. Mark location and drill five 3/16" holes in edge of A approximately 1" deep, as indicated, Illus. 220.

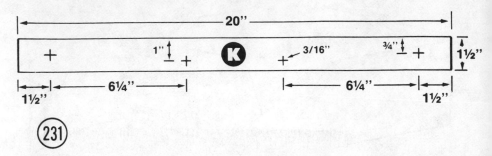

(231)

Apply oil to metal on G. Lock G in position with K. Drop four 16 penny nails through holes in KGA.

A Sakrete or equal sand mix, or type M or N mortar mix, as described on page 9,10, can be used for decorative blocks. Keep mixture on the firm side by only adding as much water as is needed. To test, squeeze a handful. If it's too dry, it will fall apart. If it's too wet, water and mortar will squeeze between the fingers. The mixture should be wet enough to compress and sufficiently stiff to hold together when form is removed.

Pack mortar around form. Tamp it with the end of a 1 x 2. When filled level with top of form, remove and use a float or trowel. Allow to set briefly, then carefully lift G. Skip a space and reposition G. This gives first block a chance to set undisturbed.

When five blocks have been poured, carefully pull nails and remove forms, Illus. 221. Allow blocks to set undisturbed for 48 hours before removing dividers D. Cut additional dividers D if you want to continue pouring. Allow blocks to remain undisturbed for three days before moving. Spray once a day with a fine mist to cure them properly.

When building a fence or outdoor partition, lay footings as described on page 50. To estimate number of courses figure each block as measuring 10⅜'' plus ⅜'' for mortar. Place blocks at ends of first course, Illus. 232. Use guide lines. Check guide line with line level, Illus. 233. Build blocks to overall height desired, Illus. 234.

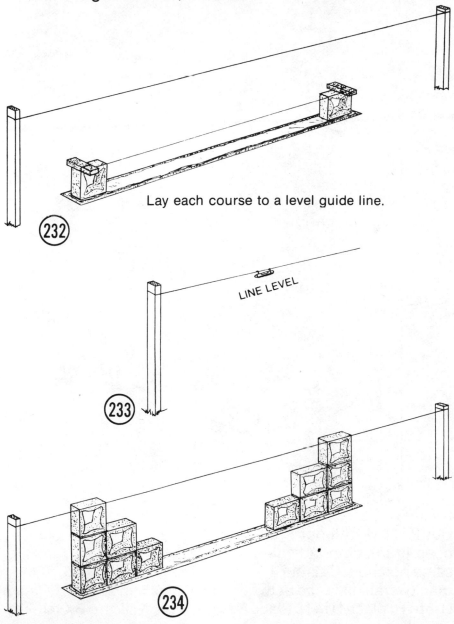

Lay each course to a level guide line.

(232)

LINE LEVEL

(233)

(234)

When blocks are used indoors as a room divider, Illus. 219, cut 2 x 4 L to overall length of blocks plus 1½'', Illus. 235. Nail L to floor. Cut M same length as L less 1½'' for P, Illus. 236 Nail M to L, P to M.

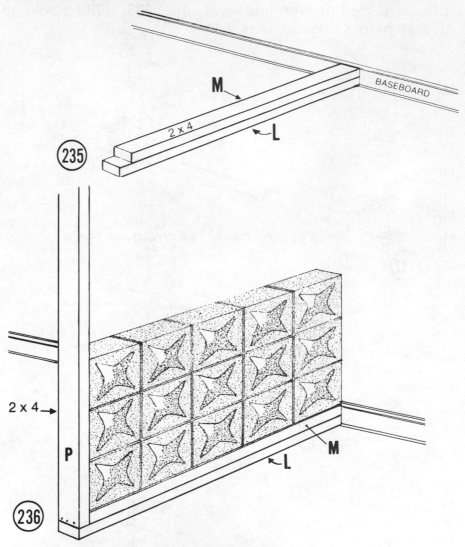

Cut 2 x 4 N to length required, Illus. 237. Drill 1'' holes 1'' deep in position indicated in N. Drill 1'' holes through R in same position. Cut four 1'' rope moldings U, Illus. 238, 1'' less than overall distance between top of block and ceiling. Place U into R. place U in N. Place N in position. Nail P to R. Nail P to

N. Toenail RN to wall. Countersink nail heads. Fill holes with wood filler. Apply matching baseboard T and shoe molding. Paint to match.

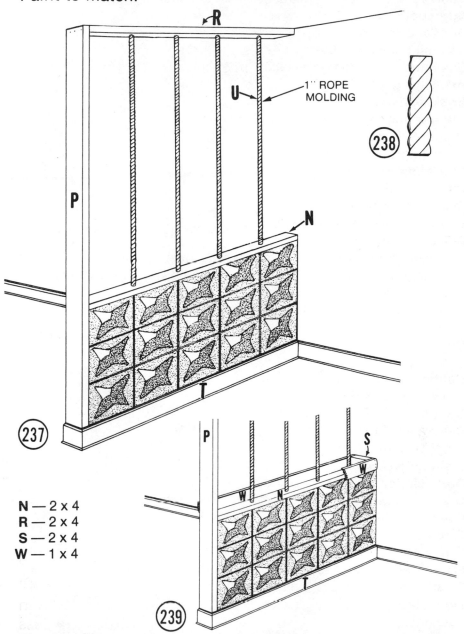

1" ROPE MOLDING

238

237

N — 2 x 4
R — 2 x 4
S — 2 x 4
W — 1 x 4

239

If you want to use top of N for potted plants, position 2 x 4 x 3½" S, Illus. 239. Nail 1 x 4 W to SP.

INDEX

ESSENTIALS OF GOOD BRICK CONSTRUCTION

◄ Spread a uniform bed of mortar over only a few brick. Furrow only lightly, if at all. Place plenty of mortar on the end of the brick to be placed. Brick is then shoved into place so that mortar is squeezed out of top of head joint.

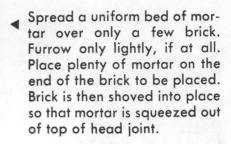

◄ After placing, mortar squeezed out of bed joint is cut off to prevent staining the wall.

◄ Concave jointer

◄ When mortar joint becomes thumbprint hard, tool with steel jointer slightly larger ◄ than the mortar joint. Concave or V joints have best weather resistance.

◄ V jointer

◄ When placing closures, place plenty of mortar on ends of brick in place and on ends of brick to be placed. Shove closure into place without disturbing brick on either side.

◄ When a wall is capped with a brick rowlock course, it is essential that all vertical joints be completely filled.

◄ rowlock

In cavity wall construction, mortar droppings should not be permitted to fall into the cavity. An aid in preventing this is to bevel the bed joint ◄ away from the cavity.

BEVELING BED JOINTS

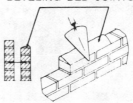

169

In metal-tied walls, a parge coat between wythes is the barrier to moisture penetration. Parging may be applied to either backup or facing units. In either case, excess mortar squeezed out of the joints should be cut off and ¼ in. to ⅜ in. of mortar trowelled on.

When brick are laid on a beveled bed joint, a minimum of mortar is squeezed out of the joint. Brick (1)—beveled joint; brick (2)—conventional joint.

The mortar squeezed from the joints on the cavity side may be plastered on to the units. This same procedure may be used for laying exterior wythes of reinforced brick walls. Mortar droppings should not be permitted in grout core.

◄ Cavity wall metal ties are embedded in bed joints as units are laid.

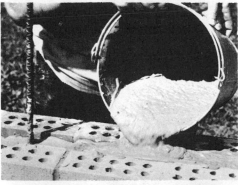

◄ In reinforced masonry, vertical steel should be placed before masonry is laid. Grout should be mixed with sufficient water to cause it to pour readily.

◄ After grout is poured, it should be puddled to consolidate it.

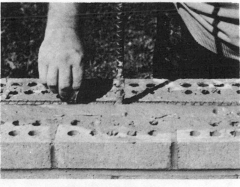

◄ Horizontal steel may be placed in grout core as wall is built.

171

CONCRETE BLOCK SIZES

A - 7⅝" **B** - 15⅝" **C** - 9⅝" **D** - 11⅝" **E** - 3⅝"

APPROXIMATE METRIC SIZE **A** - 19.4cm **B** - 39.8cm **C** - 24.4cm **D** - 29.5cm **E** - 9.2cm

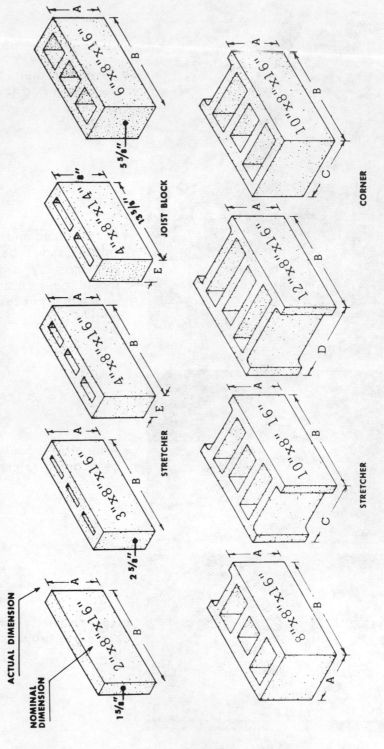

172

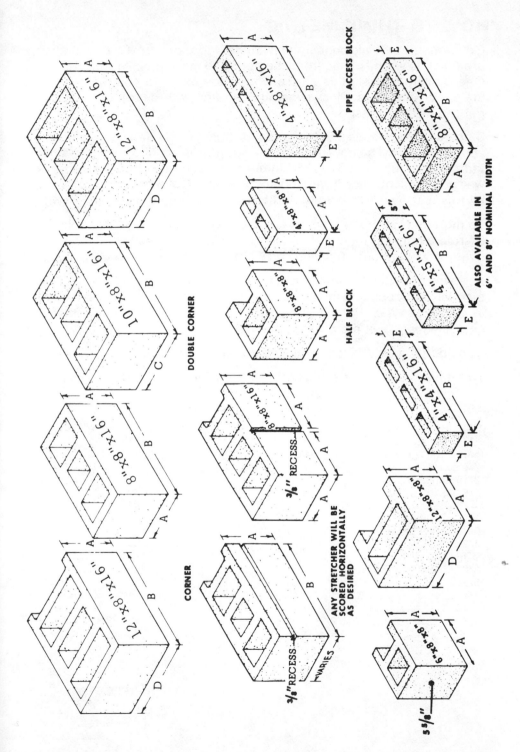

12"x8"x16"

10"x8"x16"

8"x8"x16"

12"x8"x16"

DOUBLE CORNER

CORNER

4"x8"x16"

PIPE ACCESS BLOCK

4"x8"x8"

8"x8"x8"

HALF BLOCK

8"x8"x16"

3/8" RECESS

3/8" RECESS

VARIES

ANY STRETCHER WILL BE
SCORED HORIZONTALLY
AS DESIRED

8"x4"x16"

4"x5"x16"

5"

ALSO AVAILABLE IN
6" AND 8" NOMINAL WIDTH

4"x4"x16"

12"x8"x8"

6"x8"x8"

5⅝"

173

HOW TO THINK METRIC

Government officials concerned with the adoption of the metric system are quick to warn anyone from attempting to make precise conversions. One quickly accepts this advice when they begin to convert yards to meters or vice versa. Place a metric ruler alongside a foot ruler and you get the message fast.

Since a meter equals 1.09361 yards, or 39⅜"+, the decimals can drive you up a creek. The government men suggest accepting a rough, rather than exact equivalent. They recommend considering a meter in the same way you presently use a yard. A kilometer as 0.6 of a mile. A kilogram or kilo as just over two pounds. A liter, a quart, with a small extra swig.

To more fully appreciate why a rough conversion is preferable, note the 6" rule alongside the metric rule. A meter contains 100 centimeters. A centimeter contains 10 millimeters.

As an introduction to the metric system, we used a metric rule to measure standard U.S. building materials. Since a 1 x 2 measures anywhere from ¾ to 25/32 x 1½", which is typical of U.S. lumber sizes, the metric equivalents shown are only approximate.

Consider 1" equal to 2.54 centimeters; 10" = 25.4cm.

To multiply 4¼" into centimeters: 4.25 × 2.54 = 10.795 or 10.8cm.

INCH	—	MILLIMETER
1"		25.4
15/16		23.8
7/8		22.2
13/16		20.6
3/4		19.0
11/16		17.5
5/8		15.9
9/16		14.3
1/2		12.7
7/16		11.1
3/8		9.5
5/16		7.9
1/4		6.4
3/16		4.8
1/8		3.2
1/16		1.6

INCHES	—	CENTIMETERS
1		2.54
1/8		2.9
	1/4	3.2
3/8		3.5
	1/2	3.8
5/8		4.1
	3/4	4.4
7/8		4.8
2		5.1
1/8		5.4
	1/4	5.7
3/8		6.0
	1/2	6.4
5/8		6.7
	3/4	7.0
7/8		7.3
3		7.6
1/8		7.9
	1/4	8.3
3/8		8.6
	1/2	8.9
5/8		9.2
	3/4	9.5
7/8		9.8

Inches		Centimeters
4		10.2
	1/8	10.5
	1/4	10.8
	3/8	11.1
	1/2	11.4
	5/8	11.7
	3/4	12.1
	7/8	12.4
5		12.7
	1/8	13.0
	1/4	13.3
	3/8	13.7
	1/2	14.0
	5/8	14.3
	3/4	14.6
	7/8	14.9
6		15.2
	1/8	15.6
	1/4	15.9
	3/8	16.2
	1/2	16.5
	5/8	16.8
	3/4	17.1
	7/8	17.5
7		17.8
	1/8	18.1
	1/4	18.4
	3/8	18.7
	1/2	19.1
	5/8	19.4
	3/4	19.7
	7/8	20.0
8		20.3
	1/8	20.6
	1/4	21.0
	3/8	21.3
	1/2	21.6
	5/8	21.9
	3/4	22.2
	7/8	22.5
9		22.9
	1/8	23.2
	1/4	23.5
	3/8	23.8
	1/2	24.1
	5/8	24.4
	3/4	24.8
	7/8	25.1
10		25.4
	1/8	25.7
	1/4	26.0
	3/8	26.4
	1/2	26.7
	5/8	27.0
	3/4	27.3
	7/8	27.6

Inches		Centimeters
11		27.9
	1/8	28.3
	1/4	28.6
	3/8	28.9
	1/2	29.2
	5/8	29.5
	3/4	29.8
	7/8	30.2
12		30.5
	1/8	30.8
	1/4	31.1
	3/8	31.4
	1/2	31.8
	5/8	32.1
	3/4	32.4
	7/8	32.7
14		35.6
16		40.6
20		50.8
30		76.2
40		101.6
50		127.0
60		152.4
70		177.8
80		203.2
90		228.6
100		254.0

FEET = INCHES = CENTIMETERS

FEET		INCHES		CENTIMETERS
1 =		12	=	30.5
2 =		24	=	61.0
3 =		36	=	91.4
4 =		48	=	121.9
5 =		60	=	152.4
6 =		72	=	182.9
7 =		84	=	213.4
8 =		96	=	243.8
9 =		108	=	274.3
10 =		120	=	304.8
11 =		132	=	335.3
12 =		144	=	365.8
13 =		156	=	396.2
14 =		168	=	426.7
15 =		180	=	457.2
16 =		192	=	487.7
17 =		204	=	518.2
18 =		216	=	548.6
19 =		228	=	579.1
20 =		240	=	609.6

INDEX TO MONEY-SAVING REPAIRS, IMPROVEMENTS, PATTERNS AND BOOKS
(Number designates Easi-Bild Pattern or Book)

176

INDEX TO MONEY-SAVING REPAIRS, IMPROVEMENTS, PATTERNS AND BOOKS

180

181

187

EASI-BILD® LEARN TO EARN BOOKS

#603 HOW TO BUILD A DORMER

Those who need more living space can raise a roof with a big dormer. Step-by-step directions take all the fear, mystery and inflated cost out of transforming an attic into liveable space. 82pp., 114 illus.

#605 HOW TO INSTALL PANELING

Learn to apply paneling like a pro. Build a matching wall to wall storage closet with sliding doors, a fireplace mantel, install valances with indirect lighting, even build a cedar lined storage room. 146pp., 214 illus., plus full size valance patterns simplify every step.

#606 HOW TO LAY CERAMIC TILE

Easy to follow, step-by-step directions explain how to prepare a floor or wall prior to laying ceramic tile, how to estimate material needed, cut and fit tile around tub, toilet, etc. Read, learn, then see how easily you can make ceramic tile repairs like a pro. 98pp., 137 illus.

#607 HOW TO BUILD FENCES, GATES
OUTDOOR PROJECTS

Every homeowner who appreciates privacy recognizes the need for fencing. Six different styles of colonial fencing can easily be made by tracing the full size patterns contained in this book. It also simplifies building a colonial sign post, an outdoor display cabinet - bulletin board, canopy, trellis, and much more. 162pp., 212 illus., plus full size lettering pattern.

#608 HOW TO MODERNIZE A KITCHEN

Building base and wall cabinets, then installing a continuous countertop to size space permits, enables every reader to modernize a kitchen at the lowest possible cost. Besides providing needed storage and work space, a modernized kitchen adds a sizeable Capital Gains to the value of your home. Every step explained. 82pp., 118 illus.

#609 HOW TO BUILD AN ADDITION

Creating additional living space can prove to be one of today's soundest investments. Step-by-step directions explain how to build a 12 x 16', 16 x 24' or any other size one or two story addition, with or without an outside entry. 162pp., 211 illus., simplify every step.

#611 HOW TO BUILD
GREENHOUSES - SUNHOUSES

Enjoy the fun of gardening all winter in this energy saving walk-in greenhouse. When built adjacent to a basement door or window, it captures waste heat. No costly heating is required. Step-by-step directions also explain how to build a 7'0'' x 7'4½'' walk-in sunhouse, a window greenhouse, plus a hotbed frame. 114pp., 110 illus.

#612 HOW TO BUILD WALL-TO-WALL
CABINETS, STEREO INSTALLATION
SIMPLIFIED

As every stereo enthusiast soon discovers, a wall to wall bookcase and stereo installation can cost a bundle when done by others. This book not only simplfies building cabinets to fill space available, but also takes all the mystery out of installation of components. 130pp., 165 illus.

#613 HOW TO BUILD OR ENCLOSE A PORCH

Easy to follow directions simplify building a 12 x 16' porch or to size required. Enclosing an existing porch is also explained. Since codes permit this construction, it provides a fast and economical way of creating low cost living space. When enclosed with jalousies and screens, many porches double as extra sleeping areas. 82pp., 112 illus.

#615 HOW TO MODERNIZE A BASEMENT

Whether you create a family room or turn a basement into an income producing one bedroom apartment with an outside entrance, you will find all the information needed. It explains how to install an outside entry, build stairs, frame partitions, panel walls, lay floor tile and much more. 98pp., 135 illus.

#617 CONCRETE WORK SIMPLIFIED

This book explains everything you need to know to mix concrete, floating, finishing, grooving, edging and pointing, to setting ironwork and anchor bolts. It also explains how to waterproof a basement, install a sump pump, an outside entry and make all kinds of concrete repairs. 194pp., 257 illus.

#623 HOW TO REPAIR, REFINISH
AND REUPHOLSTER FURNITURE

Learn to apply first aid to ailing furniture. Reglue joints, replace webbing, bent and broken springs, caning and cane webbing. Everything you need to know from tacks to tools. Directions also explain how to build a studio bed with a nylon cord spring, decorate furniture with provincial trim, make picture frames, etc. 98pp., 133 illus.

191

#027 HOW TO MAKE CORNICE BOARDS, DRAPERIES, VALANCES, INSTALL TRAVERSE TRACK

Full size patterns simplify making cornice and valance boards, install traverse track, indirect lighting and much more. 66pp., 117 illus.

#630 HOW TO BUILD A SPORTSMAN'S REVOLVING STORAGE CABINET

Directions simplify building a glass enclosed gun cabinet, wall racks and a 24 x 72'' revolving cabinet that stores everything from guns to clothing. Learn to make what others want to buy. 98pp., 121 illus.

#631 HOW TO BUILD PATIOS & SUNDECKS

The Easi-Bild engineered patio roof insures a free flow of air, helps keep patio degrees cooler. Step-by-step directions simplify building to size specified or to size desired. Directions also explain how to build a sundeck, privacy partition, arbor and fencing. 98pp., 133 illus.

#632 HOW TO BUILD A VACATION OR RETIREMENT HOUSE

The perfect house for a vacation or retirement. One story with full basement provides two bedrooms and an amazing amount of useable living space. When built without a basement, it contains a bedroom, kitchen, bathroom and living room. An economical solution to today's housing costs. 194pp., 170 illus.

#634 HOW TO BUILD STORAGE UNITS

Easy to follow directions simplify building wall to wall storage closets with sliding, bi-folding or pivot hinged doors. Closets can be free standing, from floor to ceiling, or built-in. Directions also simplify building an under the bed storage chest on wheels, wall wardrobe and much more. 98pp., 145 illus.

#649 HOW TO BUILD A GARDEN TOOLHOUSE, CHILD'S PLAYHOUSE

Build a free standing or lean-to tool house and take all the congestion out of your garage. Over 100 step-by-step illustrations simplify building a 6'0'' x 8'0'' walk-in tool house, a 6'4'' x 4'3'' lean-to, also a 4'0'' x 5'6'' child's playhouse. Locked storage space accommodates bicycles, riding mower, all gardening tools, insecticides, fertilizers, seeds, etc. 82pp., 107 illus.

192

#658 HOW TO BUILD KITCHEN CABINETS, ROOM DIVIDERS, CABINET FURNITURE

Handsome pole type kitchen cabinets, room dividers, bookcases, stereo cabinets, desks and other needed furniture can be built by following directions offered in this book. Stock aluminum extrusions and prefinished plywood help amateurs make like pros. 98pp., 134 illus.

#663 HOW TO BUILD A TWO CAR GARAGE, LEAN-TO PORCH, CABANA

Building a garage can prove to be a richly rewarding experience. Letters from readers who built this garage confirm the task altered their outlook on life. Many who build turn it into an income producing singles apartment. 130pp., 142 illus.

#664 HOW TO CONSTRUCT BUILT-IN AND SECTIONAL BOOKCASES

Learn to build wall-to-wall bookcases. Frame a window, door or mirror. Build from floor to ceiling or to height desired. Every step clearly illustrated. Directions also explain how to build a room divider, free standing cabinet bar and other handsome pieces. 98pp., 137 illus.

#665 HOW TO MODERNIZE AN ATTIC

Everyone who wonders how they can meet ever rising living costs finds a timely answer in this book. It explains how to build stairs, insulate and transform an attic into a liveable apartment. Directions explain how to install a skylight, build partitions, install louvers, apply paneling, and much more. 82pp., 86 illus.

#668 BRICKLAYING SIMPLIFIED

All who seek income, peace of mind, an economical solution to a costly problem or employment in a trade where opportunity is unlimited, find this book a real guide to better living. It explains how to lay bricks, a wall, walk, veneer a house, build a barbecue, etc. It turns amateurs into pros. 146pp., 212 illus.

#669 HOW TO BUILD BIRDHOUSES AND BIRD FEEDERS

Encouraging a child to build feeders and birdhouses can stimulate a lifetime interest in woodworking. Full size patterns not only simplify building but also insure success. Helping a child turn a piece of wood into a useable and saleable article builds instant self confidence. 66pp., 86 illus.

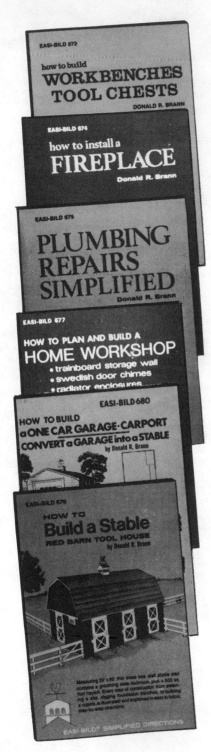

#672 HOW TO BUILD WORKBENCHES AND SAWHORSE TOOLCHEST

To economically solve costly repairs and improvements, every home, apartment and place of business needs a workbench. This encourages those who build one to build others for resale. Simplified directions show how to build 6' workbenches, with a 6' vise on one or both sides, big drawers and tool compartments, to foldaway wall benches that require a minimum of floor space. 180pp., 250 illus., plus a full size foldout pattern.

#674 HOW TO INSTALL A FIREPLACE

Everyone who wants to install a woodburning stove, build a brick fireplace or install a prefabricated metal fireplace and chimney, will find all the direction they need. Installing a chimney completely within or recessed flush with an outside wall is clearly explained and illustrated. 242pp., 354 illus.

#675 PLUMBING REPAIRS SIMPLIFIED

Homeowners who dislike having their budget and peace of mind destroyed by a faulty plumbing fixture find this book helps save time, temper and money. Everyone who has learned to bake a cake or drive a car can easily replace parts and make repairs like a pro. Read, learn, then do what directions suggest and see how much more living you get out of life. 194pp., 820 illus.

#677 HOW TO BUILD A HOME WORKSHOP

In easy to follow, step-by-step procedure, this book explains how to build base and wall cabinets to fit available space. Having all tools stored where they can be used on a sturdy workbench encourages making repairs and building many needed projects. Directions also simplify building a trainboard storage wall, radiator enclosure and other useful projects. 98pp., 133 illus.

#679 HOW TO BUILD A STABLE AND RED BARN TOOL HOUSE

Measuring 20 x 30', this three box stall stable is easy to build while it makes a dream come true. Every step of construction, from having a reason to build (to create an individual and not a joiner), selecting a site, to building the cupola, is explained, illustrated and simplified. Directions also simplify buiding an 8 x 10' or larger red barn tool house. 178pp., 197 illus.

#680 HOW TO BUILD A ONE CAR GARAGE, CARPORT, CONVERT A GARAGE INTO A STABLE

Building a one car garage with ample space for a workshop, or turning a one car garage into a two box stall stable is clearly explained. Directions tell how to raise a garage to obtain needed headroom, build a carport, lean-to toolhouse and a cupola. 146pp., 181 illus.

#682 HOW TO ADD AN EXTRA BATHROOM

This complete, easy to read guide to home plumbing helps make a dream come true for only the cost of fixtures. In easy to follow directions, it tells how to make the installation and save a bundle. Those who don't want to do any plumbing discover sizeable savings can be effected by preparing the area, then having a plumber make the installation. Read, learn, save. 162pp., 200 illus.

#683 CARPETING SIMPLIFIED

Laying carpet in your home can provide the experience needed to do the same work for others. This book explains how a pro performs each step in words and pictures every reader can easily follow. Every type of carpeting, over every kind of floor, with or without padding, is explained, illustrated and simplified. Directions explain how to carpet stairs, install protective under the carpet electronic alarm mats, and much, much more. 178pp., 223 illus.

#684 HOW TO TRANSFORM A GARAGE INTO LIVING SPACE

Transforming a garage into a living-bedroom, with a kitchen and bathroom, can provide a safe and economical solution to a costly nursing home problem. It can also become an important income producer. Step-by-step directions assume the reader has never done any of this work and explains every step. 130pp., 139 illus.

#685 HOW TO REMODEL BUILDINGS

With abandoned big city housing units available to all who are willing to rehabilitate and occupy same, this book explains how tenants can become landlords with only an investment of time and effort. It tells how to turn an abandoned multi-family building, store, garage or warehouse into rentable housing. Every step explained and illustrated. Read and learn how to become a homeowner without spending a lot of money. 258pp., 345 illus.

#690 HOW TO BUILD BARS

Building a bar offers a fun way to furnish a recreation room. Learning to build a straight, L-shaped or any of the seven bars described provides an easy way to start a part or full time business. Doing something today you didn't know how to do yesterday broadens one's sphere of activity. 162pp., 195 illus.

#694 ELECTRICAL REPAIRS SIMPLIFIED

Learning to economically make electrical repairs not only generates peace of mind, but also income in your spare time. This book takes the fear, mystery and inflated cost out of many troublesome repairs. A special feature explains how to install wiring in a dollhouse. 134pp., 218 illus.

195

#695 HOW TO INSTALL
PROTECTIVE ALARM DEVICES

Recapture peace of mind by securely protecting all doors and windows with professional alarm devices. Learn how to discourage a break-in with magnetic contacts that automatically trigger a telephone dialer to the police, sound a loud alarm bell, instantly detect movement with easy to install radar. A layman's guide to professionally installed electronic protection. 130pp., 146 illus.

#696 ROOFING SIMPLIFIED

This "business of your own" book turns amateurs into professional roofers. Learn to repair or replace an asphalt, wood or slate roof; apply roll roofing, make a roofer's safety harness, walk and work on a roof with no fear of falling, plus much more. 130pp., 168 illus.

#697 FORMS, FOOTINGS, FOUNDATIONS,
FRAMING, STAIR BUILDING

This book tells every reader how to get into the building industry. Whether you build your own house, buy a prefab or want a career in building, this book tells everything you need to know about forms, footings, foundations, framing and stair building. 210pp., 310 illus.

#751 HOW TO BUILD PET HOUSING

Encourage all who love pets to build the shelter each needs. Learn how to build a doghouse, lean-to kennel, rabbit hutch, duck-inn, parakeet cage, an all weather cat entry, plus a unique catpartment that's easy to sell, easy to rent. 178pp., 252 illus.

#753 HOW TO BUILD DOLLHOUSES
& FURNITURE

To create a memory a little girl will never forget, build one of the three dollhouses offered in this book. Those searching for a part or full time money making hobby find a ready market for dollhouses. Full size patterns simplify making fourteen pieces of dollhouse furniture. 194pp., 316 illus.

#754 HOW TO BUILD OUTDOOR FURNITURE

Easy to follow step-by-step directions, plus a big foldout full size pattern, simplify tracing and cutting all parts to exact shape required. Learn how to build curved back lawn chairs, a matching settee, four passenger lawn glider, a chaise on wheels and much, much more. 130pp., 174 illus., plus full size pattern.

196

#756 SCROLL SAW PROJECTS

Helping everyone, a child or retiree, successfully turn a piece of wood into a handsome, useable and saleable article, builds the ego. This book insures success. 27 full size patterns permit tracing all parts, then assembling each in exact position shown on the pattern. 130pp., 146 illus.

#757 HOW TO BUILD A KAYAK

Simplified directions and full size frame patterns permit building this extremely light yet sturdy kayak to three different lengths, 14'3'', 16'9'' or 18'0''. It can easily be carried on a cartop rack and used by one or two adults. Patterns insure cutting each frame to exact size required. 66pp., plus big, full size foldout pattern.

#761 HOW TO BUILD COLONIAL FURNITURE

Building colonial reproductions can provide hours of complete escape. You not only obtain furniture at a fraction of retail cost, but also enjoy every hour. Easy to follow directions and full size patterns simplify building a cobbler's bench, hutch cabinet, blanket chest, under the eaves rope bed, wall cabinet and other useful pieces. 12 colonial reproductions are offered. 258pp., 342 illus.

#763 HOW TO BUILD A TWO CAR GARAGE WITH APARTMENT ABOVE

All who seek an economical solution to a costly housing problem should read this book. It explains how to build a two car, two story garage. Directions also explain how to add a second story apartment to an existing garage. Space above provides a living, bedroom, kitchen and bathroom. Ideal for a single or couple. 194pp., 226 illus.

#771 TOYMAKING AND CHILDREN'S FURNITURE SIMPLIFIED

As every reader soon discovers, toymaking possesses a certain magic. Turning a piece of lumber into a whimsical rocking horse with a personality captures a child's imagination, triggers an interest in woodworking long before they have any idea how it was made. This book simplifies building 17 different toys and children's furniture. 194pp., 330 illus., plus a big foldout full size. pattern.

#773 HOW TO CREATE ROOM AT THE TOP

If you need one or more extra bedrooms, or an income producing apartment with outside stairs, this book explains how to make like magic. Every step, from building a dormer, installing a skylight, building and installing inside and outside stairs to a second floor, is explained and illustrated. 162pp., 239 illus.

#781 HOW TO BUILD A PATIO, PORCH AND SUNDECK

Simplified directions take all the inflated cost out of building a front or back porch, a patio to length and width specified or to size desired, a carport and sundeck. Every step, from laying footings to installation of railings, is illustrated. Directions also explain how to make screens, porch repairs, swimming pool enclosure and much more. 146pp., 220 illus.

#792 HOW TO BUILD COLLECTORS' DISPLAY CASES

Learn to build handsome, clear acrylic, museum quality, floor, table top and wall display cabinets. These provide the perfect way to display every kind of possession from dolls, china, figurines, etc. Retailers buy these cases for store use as readily as for resale. 194pp., 229 illus.

#600 COMPLETE EASI-BILD CATALOG

Anybody can do anything if they follow directions offered in Easi-Bild Books and Full Size Patterns. The catalog illustrates hundreds of patterns and home repair and improvement books. Give this book to a youth seaching to find a career and many will soon be building everything from furniture, boats, garages to houses. Getting experience in their own home encourages doing the same work for others.

#804 HOW TO BUILD BOOKCASES AND STEREO CABINETS

Takes all the mystery and over 2/3 the cost out of building bookcases and cabinets to fill any available space. 194pp., 232 illus.

#811 HOW TO BUILD GREENHOUSES — WALK-IN, WINDOW, SUNHOUSE, GARDEN TOOL HOUSE

Of special interest to everyone who enjoys the fun and relaxation of growing plants the year round. The sunhouse appeals to sun lovers who enjoy sunbathing all winter. 210pp., 229 illus.

#758 HOW TO MODERNIZE A KITCHEN, BUILD BASE AND WALL CABINETS, POLE TYPE FURNITURE

Of special interest to every homeowner who appreciates the convenience and long term Capital Gains of a completely modernized kitchen. 210pp., 263 illus.

#850 HOW TO FIND A JOB, START A BUSINESS

Of special interest to teens, retirees and anyone who wants to earn extra income. Learn to offer what others want to buy. No capital investment required.

198

how to
FIND A JOB
START A BUSINESS *
Learn to Offer what Others want to Buy
No Capital Investment Required

Learning To Earn is a course few public schools presently offer. And even fewer have instructors with any experience in starting a business in today's highly competitive society. Everyone who can read, and is willing to invest the necessary time and effort, can learn to work with concrete when they follow Easi-Bild simplified directions. Since only the strong survive, developing interest in a trade you enjoy, provides economic survival insurance.

This book is one of many that permits every reader to develop proficiency in a saleable skill without leaving home. It explains everything you need to know to lay concrete like a pro, just as the other books explain paneling, kitchen modernization, building a one or two story addition or a one, two or three bedroom house. How you live depends entirely on what you are willing to do. Regardless of past experience, success or failure, only you control your destiny. If you want to economically solve a concrete job or go into business, read, learn, then get on site experience doing work around your home.

As this book goes to press, Easi-Bild's complete library contains 7,842 pages and over 10,888 illustrations. Note complete list on pages 190 to 198, and the cross reference index to all patterns and books on pages 176 to 189.

Those who need low cost housing and all who want to make a sizeable long term Capital Gains without gambling should build a two car garage with an apartment above, or add a second story to an existing garage, as explained in Book #763. If your building site provides space at distance from property lines local codes specify, don't let local zoning con

* Excerpts from Book 850

199

you by saying, "We won't allow two family occupancy in an area zoned for single family housing." The Supreme Court ruled, in an East Cleveland, Ohio case, creating living space for a relative cannot be construed as two families.

READ, LEARN, SAVE, EARN

Build a one or two story addition with an outside entry (609); lay bricks like a pro (668), ceramic tile (606); make plumbing repairs (675); install an extra bathroom (682); do electrical work (694), roofing repairs (696); learn to build workbenches (672), outdoor furniture (754), toys (771), wall to wall bookcases (804), a three box stall stable (679), or a 16 or 18' kayak (757), and much, much more. Every step is explained and illustrated in non-technical words and pictures.

Learning to transform time into a way of life that satisfies one's physical, economic, marital and mental needs provides a lesson in living relatively few master. All too often a previous attempt that failed creates loss of confidence, a no man's land that discourages trying again. Always remember, one's capabilities and confidence, like the ever changing hands on a clock, are in continual motion. What we couldn't do yesterday is frequently easy to do today.

Consider that face you see in the mirror each morning as only one of many. You see one image. Every member of your family, friends and business associates see a different one. Getting to know The Real You, and your potential, requires a continual appraisal of all plus and minus factors. Discovering who you are, and what you can accomplish, can prove to be one of life's most exciting adventures. Remember, the letters TRY represent The Real You, and your true potential.

Learning to live a way of life many only dream of living requires following a well established formula. Every Horatio Alger rags to riches story contains the same formula. Each dreamed of what they wanted, then invested the time, thought and energy needed to materialize the dream. None were born with the needed experience. Each acquired this magical ingredient the hard way by following good direction and doing what needed to be done. This book offers every

200

reader a second brain, one that helps all who try. As computerized research confirms, getting lucky just doesn't happen. It stems from experience, perseverance, and a will to try.

Consider these basis essentials: At birth you received a body, a brain and an inheritance of time. How you use your body shapes your physical health. How you use your brain establishes a quality of life. How you invest time determines how well you will live. You may enjoy good health, possess an average or brilliant intelligence, but until you make the effort, and constantly do what needs to be done, you can't begin to enjoy your full potential. If someone in your family needs a job, or wants to start a part or full time business, READ, LEARN, THEN DO. With only an investment of time and capital to cover living expenses and needed material, this book opens doors to an experience called living.

Since people are by instinct buyers of what they need, and constantly buy more of their daily needs than anyone really sells, offering to do work for a neighbor, doctor or others, seeds the sale of your services.

Easi-Bild Books can guide you in many different spheres of activity. Those who want to build their own home can obtain easy to follow directions that simplify building a one, two or three bedroom house, Illus. 240. A complete list of material tells what to buy, while step-by-step directions explain where and when each size lumber is used.

(241)

Building a second story over a two car garage, Illus. 241, or building a two story garage from the foundation up, is no big deal. It provides great living space at low cost.

The one bedroom apartment, Illus. 242, also has great rental potential. But remember, most codes require occupation by a relative.

Easi-Bild #672 simplifies building a 6' workbench, Illus. 243, a child size, Illus. 244, a tool chest, table top bench and other comparable projects. All are easy to build, easy to sell.

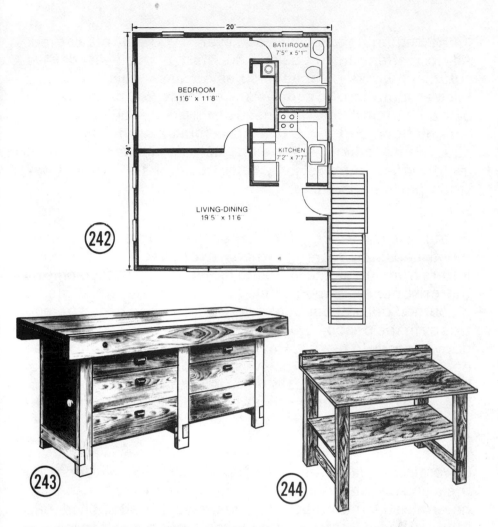

If you still lack confidence, help a neighbor or friend build a comparable project, or join an adult education class. While building a model will clarify every step, actual experience is far more helpful. Making any dream come true requires time, effort, hope in the future and prayer. All too many invest time in hope and prayer, rather than in time and effort.

Learning to offer goods or services others want to buy requires filling a need at a cost the customer can afford and is willing to pay. The selling price must compensate you for both time and material. Going into business is something anyone can do. Being successful is another story. Survival depends on knowing how and selling to those willing to pay.

In the beginning take any work, even if you only break even. All too often those seeking to start a business believe sufficient working capital inoures success. This is a totally false assumption. To achieve any success, you must not only be capable of doing what needs to be done, but also know exactly how long it will take. You must also be capable of supervising others when extra help is needed. Of equal importance, you must only select customers who will pay when payment is due.

Gaining experience is the first step. This was clearly illustrated many years ago when we received the first of three letters from an inmate in a state penetentiary. Signed only by the prisoner's number, the letter asked if we would mail a discarded copy of our bookcase book. He had begun to read a copy in the prison library, but due to time allowed, needed a copy to study in his cell. Having no funds, he asked for a free copy. Months later, we received a second letter thanking us. He reported making scale models in the prison workshop. These gave him experience and confidence. It also strengthened his desire to do this work on release.

Several years later, we received a third letter, still signed by the same prisoner number. It stated he was out of prison and determined to stay that way. On release he had applied for a job in a home improvement center. During an interview, he showed the scale models and explained how he had gained experience. By an odd coincidence, the interviewer had also worked from an Easi-Bild book when making lawn furniture. When asked what wage he expected, he promptly answered, ,"Pay whatever you can afford." His frankness in revealing a prison record, his willingness to work, and to accept whatever sum the employer could pay, cinched the interview. The letter went on to say that after two of the best years of his life he left to start his own business. It closed with this statement, "Thanks to that Easi-Bild book you mailed me many years ago, I am now, at 48, beginning to live the kind of life I should have lived the past 30 years.

The easiest way to start any business is to select an activity you enjoy, then get experience. Build samples and show them to as many people as possible. When you have found and satisfied one customer, the contact provides a key to others. Keep the contact alive. Their friends, neighbors, church and business associates usually live comparable lives and experience comparable needs. A satisfied customer is your most valuable business asset.

Since people tend to have the same needs, at about the same time, you begin to hit pay dirt when you tune your effort to seasonal goods and services. An early spring or summer display of lawn furniture, Illus. 245, chairs, settees, chaise on wheels, picnic tables, displayed alongside a well traveled road, or in a busy gas station, can attract many customers. Build samples of all the outdoor furniture offered in Book #754. Attempt to place these on display wherever a cooperative retailer or business has the space, the traffic, and a willingness to work with you. Thumbtack a sign to each piece stating your name, address, telephone number. Mention all furniture will be painted color customer requests. Pay a commission to each "agent" who makes a sale.

Use the same approach to sell adult and child size workbenches built according to Book #672. An early fall effort usually generates a lot of pre-Christmas business. High packing and shipping costs on work-benches, purchased from an out of town supplier, add much to its retail price. This enables you to price yours under competition and still make a normal margin of profit. Since a scale model generates a lot of interest, one reader wrote to tell how he placed two scale models on his desk prior to retirement. As traffic manager of a large corporation, he was constantly meeting with associates. Almost everyone picked up

and examined the model of the adult and child size workbench. When informed he planned on building work-benches on retirement, he began getting orders. The night of his "retirement party," he received fourteen orders.

Since each new business must first find a need, then fill it, the price you charge must be in direct competition to others offering the same product or service. Every selling price must cover cost of material, labor and insurance. If you hire help, be sure to include liability and unemployment insurance, social security, state and city taxes, etc. Always check the price of comparable goods offered in a mail order catalog, and in local stores. Don't plan on getting rich on your first sales. Use these to gain experience. If you lack working capital, ask the first few customers to buy material directions specify. Level with each customer. Explain you are just starting and need the work. If you only earn a minimum hourly wage rate, it could still be a very sound investment of your time.

LEARNING TO EARN courses should be endorsed by every parent. These should be rated as important as reading, writing and arithmetic. Encourage local parent and teacher associations to sponsor job clinics wherein every home-owner, retailer, wholesaler, office or factory within the school district, lists all help wanted jobs. Each school should mimeograph and post these lists on a bulletin board so every student seeking part time work can apply.

Since every problem requires a solution, learning to focus one's mentalens, the mind's eye, provides an exercise that helps relieve tension. Developing the strength and desire to depend on no one but yourself, to accept direction and make whatever effort needs to be made, helps rebuild an ego, provides insurance against despair. No trust fund or inheritance from a rich uncle can insure a more constructive way of life.

Everyone desirous of getting into the repair and home improvement business soon discovers seasonal changes create many customers. When a high wind or heavy rain does extensive damage, finding a roofer willing to make repairs, at a cost the homeowner can afford, creates new business opportunities. As Book #696 Roofing Simplified clearly explains, most people are afraid to climb a high ladder. Even more fear walking and working on a roof. The first chapter of Book #696 tells how to make a rope body harness, Illus. 246, how to secure and use a roofer's safety  line, Illus. 247. When you put on the body harness and use the safety line, you can climb a ladder, walk and work on a roof in far more safety than you can cross many city streets.

One of the easiest ways to develop a roofing business is to contact home improvement retailers who sell roofing. While some only sell material, others sell labor and material. If a local retailer doesn't show any interest, and a roofer gives you a hard time saying, "We can only hire skilled roofers or selected apprentices," print some 8½ x 11" ads. Print the same kind of message every roofer inserts in the yellow pages of a telephone directory, or local newspaper.

Prior to or at the start of the rainy season, place one of these 8½ x 11" ads in every mailbox in that part of town where previous storms have done the most damage. When a local newspaper shows storm pictures, note the neighborhood covered. Nature generates much fear and thus seeds many customers for a roof repair or replacement. Harness nature's power, she can be your best salesman. Always place your message in those mailboxes where the property indicates the owner can afford to pay for services offered.

If you don't own a home and have no place to test your skill as a roofer, still make the body harness and become thoroughly familiar with the roofer's safety line. When you phone an established roofer or retailer for an appointment, explain you are looking for work and would like to talk to whoever does the hiring. The most favorable response invariably comes shortly after a storm has done considerable damage. Homeowners and pros give far more consideration when their need is urgent. In each interview with a homeowner, roofing company or retailer, mention the fact that you know how to work in safety on a roof and can make roofing and gutter repairs. This is a big plus especially with roofers. Few can find applicants with this capability. Regardless of what they say about roofing being a "trade that takes years to learn," speak up and say, "I know how to apply roofing."

If you decide to work as an independent, talk to an insurance agent. Find out what kind of insurance you should carry to protect your customers against any damage that may occur while you do the work. It's up to you to protect each customer. A knowledgeable homeowner will want to know the name of the insurance carrier, policy number and amount of coverage your insurance provides before agreeing to your doing any work. In your ad, mention the fact that you are a completely Insured Roofer. This helps generate confidence.

Another area that offers considerable potential is the tool rental store. Since they rent extension ladders, scaffolding and other special tools, they frequently have customers who need help.

Apply the same approach to any specialized service you want to offer. Reading Book #606, How to Lay Ceramic Tile, can put you into a very profitable area of activity. Laying ceramic tile on a bathroom or kitchen floor or wall isn't difficult. And it offers a good return for every hour invested. While you will need a tile cutter and other tools specified, these are readily available from most tile retailers and tool rental stores.

EASI-BILD 606
how to lay
CERAMIC TILE
Donald R. Brann

This book takes the mystery out of laying ceramic tile. It explains every step in language everyone understands. Whether you do part, all or none of the work, substantial savings can be made by estimating and buying the required. Directions tell how to tile floors, walls, countertops, around fireplace mantels, plus patios — also tells how to replace broken or loose tile.

Now consider the potential. Most homeowners who would like a modernized kitchen don't have sufficient space. This requires building an addition. And again, fate lends a helping hand. Homeowners who have an aging parent housing problem, or need a separate apartment for a divorced son or daughter, will want to build a one or two story addition with an outside entry, as simplified in Book #609. When the cost of putting a parent in a nursing home is compared to building a two story addition, people buy; you don't have to sell. But you do have to explain zoning restrictions, how they must obtain a permit as suggested in Books #609 and #763.

The parent is usually happy to pay all costs for the expanded countrystyle kitchen with a fireplace and the one bedroom, bathroom and kitchenette apartment with an outside entry. If the parent doesn't make this investment, the government takes it all away when a will is probated.

As previously mentioned, don't let a local zoning board give you a hard time getting a permit. If the addition can be

209

constructed the proper distance from the property line, and "hardship," i.e., housing a relative, is involved, the law is on your side.

Shop local competition. Read the latest magazines to keep abreast with current kitchen styles. If local firms use prefinished hardwood paneling, read Book #605 and offer same. If tile kitchen floors and countertops are in demand, read Book #606. If the customer wants a low cost floor, read Book #615 and install asphalt tile.

When you visit a prospect, analyze their needs and potential. If they mention "space to entertain," a countrystyle kitchen could be what they are seeking. Since they will have talked to competitive kitchen modernizers, be sure to estimate all your costs before giving them a firm estimate. In figuring this, remember, in many cases when old cabinets are removed you may find rotted flooring and floor joists, holes in plaster walls, and other structural damage that can materially increase overall costs. Being frank and explaining these facts prior to getting a contract, then mentioning same in the agreement you draw up, builds confidence and goodwill.

If the family is looking for a quality installation, make inquiry to find out if there is a music lover in the family. Suggest installation of a ceiling speaker so it can be connected to a stereo system as explained in Book #612.

Crime is on the rise, suggest installation of the wiring contacts and bells needed for a burglary alarm as detailed in Book #695.

Book #674 explains how to install a prefabricated chimney needed for a woodburning stove or fireplace, while Book #668 explains how to build a masonry fireplace and chimney.

 **MUCH GOOD LUCK!**